Mental Arithm

Teacher's Guide

Ann Montague-Smith

Schofield & Sims

First published in 2013

Copyright © Schofield & Sims Limited 2013

Author: **Ann Montague-Smith**

Ann Montague-Smith has asserted her moral right under the Copyright, Designs and Patents Act, 1988, to be identified as the author of this work.

Schofield & Sims would like to extend its grateful thanks to **Andrew Dunn,** who wrote the **Entry test, Entry test marking key, Group record sheet** and all the **General resources** contained in this book. These items were first published in the **I can do maths Teacher's Guide** (ISBN 978 07217 1115 7, copyright © Schofield & Sims Limited 2007) and are used with the kind permission of the author. The **I can do** teaching method is one way of using a workbook series such as **Mental Arithmetic** or its companion series, **English Skills**. For further details, visit www.schofieldandsims.co.uk

British Library Catalogue in Publication Data:
A catalogue record for this book is available from the British Library.

Commissioning by **Carolyn Richardson Publishing Services** (www.publiserve.co.uk)
Design by **Ledgard Jepson Limited**
Printed in the UK by **Wyndeham Gait Limited,** Grimsby, Lincolnshire

ISBN 978 07217 1211 6

Contents

Introduction

Assessment resources

Contents pages from each of the seven pupil books
Entry test
Entry test marking key
Diagnostic checks for each of the seven pupil books
Marking keys to the Diagnostic checks for each of the seven pupil books,
with Activity prompts

General resources

Entry test Group record sheet
Language of maths sheets from each of the seven pupil books
Units of measurement – and money
Number line: −10 to +10
Number line: 0 to 100
Counting square
Multiplication square
Months of the year
Fractions chart
Fraction equivalencies
Time
Ordering numbers
Area
Perimeter
Two-dimensional (2-D) shapes and three-dimensional (3-D) shapes
Parts of a circle
Coordinates (use this copymaster to write your own coordinates practice questions)

Glossary

Full list of the Schofield & Sims Mental Arithmetic books

Introduction

1. Description

Mental Arithmetic for Key Stage 2

Schofield & Sims Mental Arithmetic provides carefully graded practice in mathematics. Comprising seven pupil books with accompanying books of answers, plus this one **Teacher's Guide** covering the whole series, it is designed primarily for Key Stage 2 pupils, with Books 1 to 4 aimed at pupils in Years 3 to 6. However, the Introductory Book may also be suitable for use at Key Stage 1, and Books 5 and 6 provide a bridge to Key Stage 3. All the books may be used flexibly, to suit your own purposes: a few ideas for use are given on pages 6 and 9 – and to these you will be able to add many other ideas of your own.

The term 'mental arithmetic' is usually associated with spoken questions that the pupil works out in his or her head before providing a verbal or written answer. However, pupils using **Schofield & Sims Mental Arithmetic** read the questions themselves and often use rough paper to calculate their answers, which are then written down so you, the teacher, are able to check them later.

This **Teacher's Guide** is designed to support you as you use **Schofield & Sims Mental Arithmetic** in your classroom. It introduces the series, describes how the Entry test may be used to select the right pupil book for each pupil or class, and explains how the books are best used on a day-to-day basis. It also tells you how to use the seven Diagnostic checks, which relate separately to each pupil book and are administered if a pupil is having difficulties.

Two sets of resources are provided. The **Assessment resources** support you in your selection of the most appropriate pupil book. As well as providing copymasters for the Entry test and Diagnostic checks, and marking keys for all these items, this section also includes Contents pages from each of the seven pupil books. These will show you in detail the areas of maths that are covered in each book. The **General resources** provide a Group record sheet and include a variety of other useful items that will help you to develop pupils' maths skills.

Using the series with older and younger pupils

At Key Stage 3

By popular request, Schofield & Sims provides the **Mental Arithmetic** pupil books in an alternative format – for use at Key Stage 3 and beyond with students who may be struggling with the work normally given to their age group. The content of this second set of books is exactly the same, but the covers are designed for older students and bear the slightly revised title, **Essential Mental Arithmetic**.

Essential Mental Arithmetic can also be used as a baseline skills programme at the start of Key Stage 3, or at the beginning of any maths-related course, to bring all students up to the same level before further teaching begins.

The **Mental Arithmetic** books of answers are fully compatible with the **Essential Mental Arithmetic** pupil books. Similarly the content of this **Teacher's Guide** is as applicable to **Essential Mental Arithmetic** as it is to the main **Mental Arithmetic** series. The Entry test and Diagnostic checks provide excellent support for Key Stage 3 students and their teachers.

At Key Stage 1

Schofield & Sims Mental Arithmetic may also be used with a few pupils in Key Stage 1 who are more competent in maths than most of their peers. Again, this book will help you to establish what the pupils already know. You might begin by using the Diagnostic check for the Introductory book – or for a later book if that seems appropriate.

Full range available

A full list of all **Mental Arithmetic** and **Essential Mental Arithmetic** books is provided at the back of this guide. Please note that an additional series, **First Mental Arithmetic**, is available for use at Key Stage 1 and with those pupils in Key Stage 2 who find the **Mental Arithmetic** series too difficult. For further details of the full range of books available, visit www.schofieldandsims.co.uk or telephone 01484 607080.

The 'I can do' teaching method

Below the list of **Mental Arithmetic** books at the back of this **Teacher's Guide** you will find a reference to the **I can do** teaching method. This is one way of using a series such as **Mental Arithmetic** to provide pupils with intensive daily practice. If you are interested in exploring the method, you can watch a specially-made film about **I can do maths** on the Schofield & Sims website **www.schofieldandsims.co.uk**: select **numeracy** at Key Stage 2 and **I can do maths**, then scroll down to find the video link.

> Schofield & Sims is sometimes asked for an indication of the National Curriculum level that pupils may have reached on completion of each **Mental Arithmetic** pupil book. By popular request, this information is now provided as a free download from the **Mental Arithmetic** pages of the Schofield & Sims website (www.schofieldandsims.co.uk). Please note, however, that the information is for your guidance only. It must be used only in conjunction with your own assessment of a pupil's knowledge and understanding and his or her ability to apply this theoretical knowledge in practical ways.

2. Purpose

Developing understanding

Schofield & Sims Mental Arithmetic is for use alongside your existing maths lessons. It gives pupils the opportunity to develop their understanding of concepts already learned by providing carefully differentiated questions in the volume necessary for intensive and regular use.

Please bear in mind that any new areas must be taught thoroughly before pupils meet them in the **Mental Arithmetic** books. This will give pupils the chance to do well, showing you what they know as well as what they may have forgotten. The books will also highlight those areas where pupils' understanding is poor and they need further help.

In addition, **Schofield & Sims Mental Arithmetic** reinforces and develops pupils' understanding of maths vocabulary. Each pupil book includes a 'language of maths' glossary and all seven of these pages are reproduced in the **General resources** section of this **Teacher's Guide**. The definitions are also provided as a single photocopiable Glossary, found at the back of this book.

Personalised learning

Mental Arithmetic makes it easy for you to provide differentiated work for different abilities within a class or group. Pupils working significantly above or below age-related expectations may work on the book best suited to their needs. This means that all pupils will be working at their own level and pace, giving you the time to support those who need your help. The more able will extend their knowledge and skills, while the less able will have time to reinforce earlier learning and build their confidence rather than struggling to keep up with general class sessions.

Monitoring progress, rewarding achievement

The **Mental Arithmetic** pupil books provide a permanent record of work, and the pupils are encouraged both to monitor their own progress and to take a pride in the development of their maths skills.

If you wish to generate new interest in and greater enthusiasm for maths in your class, you might think about setting up a Maths Challenge. Such a challenge would require pupils to complete the tests competitively – using the same pupil book if class members are of similar ability, or different books if the class is of mixed ability. Recognition could be given either for the most marked improvement or for the highest cumulative test scores over a term or year. If your whole school uses **Mental Arithmetic**, you might consider extending the Maths Challenge across all the Key Stage 2 classes.

If you wish to acknowledge and reward those pupils whose achievements – at whatever level – are especially significant, you may download blank certificate masters from the **Mental Arithmetic** pages of the Schofield & Sims website (www.schofieldandsims.co.uk).

3. Structure

Pupil book structure

The seven pupil books are carefully graded, from **Mental Arithmetic Introductory Book** to **Mental Arithmetic 6**. Each book comprises three sections with 12 tests in each. The tests become more difficult, but the increase in difficulty is gradual. The books are fully compatible with the Key Stage 2 mathematics curriculum.

Books 1 to 5 also include two 10-minute Progress Tests (with Results Charts) and final Check-up Tests that help you to identify gaps in understanding. In the Introductory Book and Book 6, these extra tests are replaced by Just Facts tests and Revision Tests respectively.

Please note: Pupils working towards the objectives for an earlier year should use the appropriate pupil book. There is no need for all members of the class to be working on the same book at the same time.

Individual test structure

Each test is in three parts, A, B and C:

- **Part A:** contains questions where the use of language is kept to a minimum, and symbols and numbers are used.

- **Part B:** contains questions where mathematical language is used.

- **Part C:** contains written questions that involve one- or two-step problem solving.

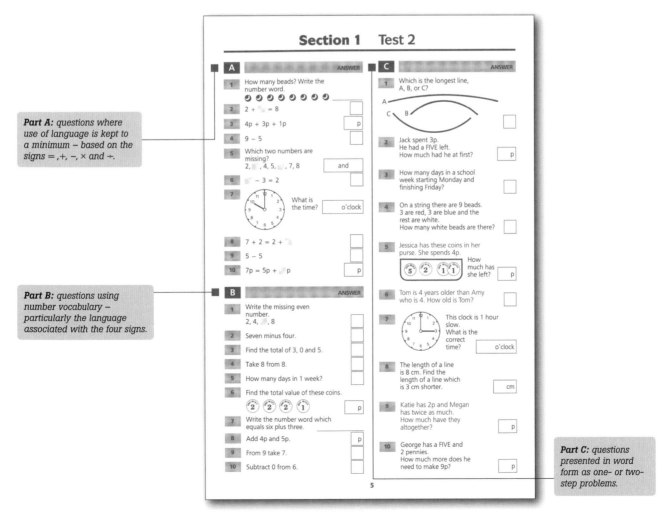

Part A: questions where use of language is kept to a minimum – based on the signs =, +, −, × and ÷.

Part B: questions using number vocabulary – particularly the language associated with the four signs.

Part C: questions presented in word form as one- or two-step problems.

This page is from **Mental Arithmetic 1**.

4. Getting started

Administering the Entry test

The Entry test is designed to help you to identify the **Mental Arithmetic** book that will best suit each pupil. You may wish to test all the class or, if you are already using the series, only those whose competency in mathematics you are unsure of. If a new pupil joins your class during the year, administer the test to decide which **Mental Arithmetic** book is the most appropriate.

Before administering the Entry test, ensure that you have available for each pupil:

* a sharp pencil, a photocopy of the test and some rough paper for working out

* a reading book, in case the pupil finishes the test early.

Explain to the pupil or the class the following points:

* the purpose of the test is to make sure that the maths work they do on a daily basis is at a suitable level – not too easy or too difficult for them

* only the individual and the teacher will know the results of the test

* the test is not timed but is likely to take about an hour

* the questions are arranged to become increasingly difficult as they work through the test

* there will come a point where they are unable to answer any more questions – and at this point they may read quietly so as not to disturb others who are still working

* they should try to do their best.

You may then distribute the Entry test and tell pupils to start.

Marking the Entry test

Use the Entry test marking key to mark the test. One mark is given for each correct answer. Where a question has two parts, give half a mark for each part. On the pupil's test sheet write the mark for each question in the grey box adjoined to the answer box. Total the marks given in each column then add the column marks to find the total score.

When everyone's test is marked, note the results on a photocopy of the Group record sheet. The table at the bottom of the Group record sheet provides best fit suggestions as follows:

Entry test score interpretation table

Entry test total score	Schofield & Sims Mental Arithmetic book
0–15	Introductory Book (red)
16–30	Book 1 (dark green)
31–50	Book 2 (blue)
51–70	Book 3 (light green)
71–90	Book 4 (dark blue/purple)
91+	Book 5 (orange)

All those pupils who score more than 90 on the Entry test should be asked to work on Book 5 for at least a few weeks – so you can ensure that they are comfortable with all the concepts covered. Those whose high scores continue for a period of a few weeks or longer should be moved on to Book 6 (grey).

Using the pupil books

The books may be used in many different ways. For example, they may be used for:

- **individual work**, with pupils who are confident with the maths concepts covered. Encourage them to think through question content, maths vocabulary and methods for solution. Challenge them to work quickly and accurately, demonstrating and applying their knowledge.

- **maths recovery work**, where the Entry test, Diagnostic checks and then the pupil books are used to assess new or struggling pupils and to raise the standard of their work.

- **paired work**, with pupils lacking confidence in some concepts. Pair each pupil with another of similar ability. Ask them to work independently but, if one of them is unsure, encourage discussion of the question and possible methods for answering it. Provide scrap paper for workings out.

- **group work**, with pupils working on the same book. Once the pupils have answered a set of questions, assign a teaching assistant to work through each one with the group, using a whiteboard or flipchart. This gives pupils the chance to use appropriate maths vocabulary in explaining their solutions. Less confident pupils are able, with assistance, to rehearse methods.

- **homework**, based on specific pages, such as a test begun in class. Parents should encourage pupils to explain their working methods – particularly for answering the problem-solving questions from Part C.

The daily Mental Arithmetic sessions

Try to make a time each day when the pupils work through part of a test. Some schools find that a session of 20 to 30 minutes is best and some schools ask the pupils to start this as they come into the classroom at the beginning of the day.

When you first introduce the books, tell the pupils that:

- they should do their best to answer the questions

- they can refer to you or to another adult if they need some guidance

- they can talk to a friend to discuss any question that they find difficult

- if a question is causing difficulty they can miss it out.

Group marking sessions

Many teachers organise weekly marking sessions in which all the tests completed during the week are marked together, as follows:

- as you prepare for the session, make sure that you have with you – for quick reference – the relevant books of answers

- ask the pupils to open their **Mental Arithmetic** books at the appropriate place and to sit facing the board or whiteboard

- work through the three parts of the test, reading out each question in turn to ensure that everyone is focused and understands the vocabulary

- invite one pupil to answer the question and to explain how he or she worked out the answer

- clearly explain to the pupils whether this answer is correct or not, and tell the pupils to mark their own answers accordingly

- other pupils may have used a different method from the one demonstrated: discuss which method is the most efficient and why

- if a pupil gives the wrong answer, model the correct answer on the board or whiteboard.

If a pupil regularly, over five or six weeks, scores nearly full marks you should consider moving him or her to the next book in the series.

Using the Diagnostic checks

A one-page Diagnostic check, covering key concepts, is provided for each book: see the **Assessment resources** section of this **Teacher's Guide**. Use the checks with any individuals or groups of pupils who have struggled with the maths concepts in the **Mental Arithmetic** book that they are currently using.

The questions in each Diagnostic check are grouped by topic. The relevant Marking key provides catch-up activities for each topic, in the form of Activity prompts. These recommend ways in which you or another adult can help the pupil with the concept that he or she may not have understood. After using the prompt, give further examples of the concept for the pupil to think through. Begin with simple items and move to more complex ones. Many other activities may be developed from these initial ideas. Use the activities diagnostically to assess the pupil's understanding of the concept.

Some Activity prompts suggest that, at first, pupils use their fingers to keep track of the mental count. Over time, encourage the pupils to visualise the number line instead.

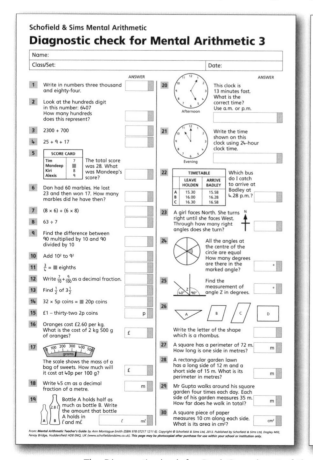
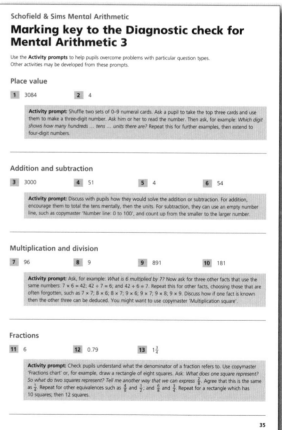

The Diagnostic check for Book 3, and part of the accompanying Marking key with Activity prompts.

General resources

The language of maths copymasters define the key terms used in **Mental Arithmetic**. Further general copymasters may be copied as handouts or enlarged and used as posters. Where a copymaster is referred to in an Activity prompt, its title appears in inverted commas.

Schofield & Sims Mental Arithmetic

Assessment resources

Use these resources to help you decide which **Mental Arithmetic** pupil book a pupil or class should begin with.

The pages marked with the Schofield & Sims copyright details may be photocopied after purchase for use within your school or institution only.

Contents   Schofield & Sims Mental Arithmetic Introductory Book

Contents

Schofield & Sims Mental Arithmetic 1

Contents
Schofield & Sims Mental Arithmetic 2

Contents Schofield & Sims Mental Arithmetic 3

Contents

Schofield & Sims Mental Arithmetic 4

Contents

Schofield & Sims Mental Arithmetic 5

Contents
Schofield & Sims Mental Arithmetic 6

Section 1 **Section 1 Achievement Chart**

Tests 1 to 12 covering revision of the *Introductory Book* and Books 1 to 5, plus the topics listed under 'Note for Students and Teachers', below.

Revision Test 1

Section 2 **Section 2 Achievement Chart**

Tests 1 to 12 covering revision of the *Introductory Book* and Books 1 to 5, plus the topics listed below.

Revision Test 2

Section 3 **Section 3 Achievement Chart**

Tests 1 to 12 covering revision of the *Introductory Book* and Books 1 to 5, plus the topics listed below.

Revision Test 3

Note for Students and Teachers

The organisation of the tests in this book differs from that in the earlier books:
- the Part A and B tests follow the same topic order from section to section, as shown below
- the Part C tests take the form of longer questions based on a problem-solving approach, allowing the topics introduced in Parts A and B to be developed in more depth.

Part A   **Questions 1–4: Number:** Four rules with positive and negative integers (including remainders, brackets). Numbers in words and figures; index notation, standard notation. Fractions, decimals, percentages, ratios, mixed numbers. Equivalence; ordering (including negative numbers, symbols <, >).

Questions 5–9: Computation: involving fractions, decimals, percentages and ratios. Four rules with decimals (including remainders, brackets). Approximations to significant figures/decimal places; estimations.

Questions 10–12: Algebra: Substitutions, simple equations; squares, square roots, cubes, factors, multiples, primes, series.

Part B   **Questions 1–2: Money:** Four rules, shopping, costing, sharing, ratio. Percentages, profit, loss; buying and selling; interest. Deposits, instalments; sales, discounts; foreign exchange.

Questions 3–6: Measures: Metric units, imperial units, conversions. Time. Compound measures.

Questions 7–9: Space and shape: Circumference, perimeter, area, volume of simple 2-D/3-D shapes. Angles of 2-D shapes including circles. Pythagoras' theorem. Symmetry and order.

Question 10: Approximations

Part C   **Questions 1–12: Longer problem-solving questions: Coordinates:** identification, location; reflections, translations, mappings. **Handling data:** graphs, tables, spreadsheets. **Scale drawings:** maps, charts. **Probability. Number puzzles:** number properties (revision); mathematical symbols. **Practical situations:** measures: length, area, money.

Schofield & Sims Mental Arithmetic

Entry test

Name:

Class/Set: Date:

ANSWER

1   + =

2   + =

3   ▦ + ⊙ = 3

4   5p + 1p =   p

5   10p – 1p =   p

6   ▦ p – 1p = 4p   p

7   ▦ Write the name of this shape.

8   Which pencil is longer?

    A
    B

9   Which day comes after Tuesday?

10 What time is it?
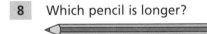
                                   o'clock

11 Count the sticks. How many?

12 3 + 6

13 7 – 2

14 5p + 2p + 1p   p

15 9p – 6p   p

16 8 = 5 + ▦

17 4 × 1

18 5 = 9 – ▦

19 2 + 2 + 2 + 2

20 6 + 2

21 5 – 2

ANSWER

22 What is the time?

23 Find the total number of dots.
    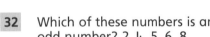 and

24 Take 0 from 7

25 Write the word for the missing number. 3, 5, ▦, 9

26 Four more than five.

27 How many must be taken from 5 to leave 3?

28 To eight add zero.

29 What number equals double 2?

30 From 6 subtract 3

31 Find the difference between 3 and 8

32 Which of these numbers is an odd number? 2, 4, 5, 6, 8

33 6 + 4 + 8

34 15p – 8p   p

35 ½ hour = ▦ min   min

36 5p + 5p + 2p + 2p   p

37 ½ of 14

38 5 TWOS = ▦ FIVES   FIVES

39 5 + 9 = 10 + ▦

40 3 + ▦ = 12

41 7 cm + 8 cm = 10 cm + ▦ cm   cm

42 6 × 2 = 3 × ▦

43 Add 5, 4 and 9

44 Subtract 7 from 16

45 Find the sum of 10p, 5p and 2 TWOS.   p

46 How many FIVES are worth 20p?   FIVES

47	Increase 17 by 8	
48	How much more than 9p are 3 TWOS and a FIVE?	p
49	1 hour = 30 min + ■ min	min
50	How many halves in 9 whole ones?	
51	Three times the value of a coin equals 15p. What is the value of the coin?	p
52	How many metres are there in (a) 1 km (b) $\frac{1}{2}$ km?	(a) m (b) m
53	Write in words the number shown on the abacus picture.	
54	$(3 \times 9) + 6$	
55	$5 + ■ = 13$	
56	9 cm 4 mm = ■ mm	mm
57	237p = £ ■	£
58	80×10	
59	$(18 \div 3) - (16 \div 4)$	
60	3 TENS − 23p	p
61	28p + 80p = £ ■	£
62	£6 = ■ FIFTIES	FIFTIES
63	1 h 50 min = ■ min	min
64	300 − 175	
65	Add four hundred to one thousand and ten. Answer in figures.	
66	Increase 29 by 33	
67	Find the change from a FIFTY after spending 28p.	p
68	Multiply £0.40 by 8	£
69	Write 87 to the nearest 10	
70	Divide 200 by 10	
71	Write as £s the sum of 26p, 28p and 50p.	£
72	27p = ■ FIVES plus 6 TWOS	FIVES
73	How many tenths in $1\frac{1}{2}$?	TENTHS
74	Subtract 36p from £1	p
75	How many TWOS have the same value as 4 TENS?	TWOS
76	Find the cost of one if 10 cost £1	p
77	Write in words the number shown on the abacus picture.	
78	17 + 8 + 16	
79	965 − 605	
80	$(8 \times 7) + 5$	
81	$(56 - 8) \div 8$	
82	$\frac{7}{10}$ of 100 g	g
83	$1\frac{3}{4}$ h = ■ min	min
84	£1.45 = ■ FIVES	FIVES
85	4 km 350 m = ■ m	m
86	850 g + ■ g = $1\frac{1}{2}$ kg	g
87	£7.09 = ■ pennies	p
88	■ TENS + 6 TWOS = £1.82	TENS
89	Write in figures the number twelve thousand and eight.	
90	How many groups of 9 are there in 6 sixes?	
91	What is the difference in pence between £$\frac{1}{5}$ and £$\frac{1}{4}$?	p
92	How many tens are equal to 1070?	
93	Find the total of 53p and £1.37	£
94	By how many g is $\frac{1}{2}$ kg heavier than 280 g?	g
95	Find the cost of 9 articles at 13p each.	£
96	How many mm are there in 10.7 cm?	mm
97	How much change from a FIFTY after spending 17p and 16p?	p
98	Change to 24-hour clock times (a) 9.35 a.m. (b) 8.50 p.m.	(a) (b)
99	Find the smallest number which will divide by both 6 and 8 without a remainder.	
100	What sum of money when multiplied by 7 equals £1.12?	p

Test total score:

Schofield & Sims Mental Arithmetic book:

Entry test marking key

Schofield & Sims Mental Arithmetic

1	7
2	9
3	2 or ∶
4	6p
5	9p
6	5p
7	square
8	A
9	Wednesday
10	5 o'clock *or* five o'clock
11	7
12	9
13	5
14	8p
15	3p
16	3
17	4
18	4
19	8
20	8
21	3
22	7.30 *or* half past seven
23	7
24	7
25	seven

26	9
27	2
28	8
29	4
30	3
31	5
32	5
33	18
34	7p
35	30 min
36	14p
37	7
38	2 FIVES
39	4
40	9
41	5 cm
42	4
43	18
44	9
45	19p
46	4 FIVES
47	25
48	2p
49	30 min
50	18

51	5p
52	(a) 1000 m (b) 500 m
53	two thousand and fifty-four
54	33
55	8
56	94 mm
57	£2.37
58	800
59	2
60	7p
61	£1.08
62	12 FIFTIES
63	110 min
64	125
65	1410
66	62
67	22p
68	£3.20
69	90
70	20
71	£1.04
72	3 FIVES
73	15 TENTHS
74	64p
75	20 TWOS

76	10p
77	six thousand and thirteen
78	41
79	360
80	61
81	6
82	70 g
83	105 min
84	29 FIVES
85	4350 m
86	650 g
87	709p
88	17 TENS
89	12 008
90	4
91	5p
92	107
93	£1.90
94	220 g
95	£1.17
96	107 mm
97	17p
98	(a) 09:35 (b) 20:50
99	24
100	16p

From: **Mental Arithmetic Teacher's Guide** (ISBN 978 07217 1211 6). Copyright © Schofield & Sims Ltd, 2013. First published in the **I can do maths Teacher's Guide** by Andrew Dunn, copyright © Schofield & Sims Ltd, 2007. Published by Schofield & Sims Ltd, Dogley Mill, Fenay Bridge, Huddersfield HD8 0NQ, UK (www.schofieldandsims.co.uk). **This page may be photocopied after purchase for use within your school or institution only.** This same material but with **Essential Mental Arithmetic** branding may be downloaded from the **Essential Mental Arithmetic** pages of the Schofield & Sims website.

Schofield & Sims Mental Arithmetic

Diagnostic check for Mental Arithmetic Introductory Book

Name:	
Class/Set:	Date:

ANSWER

Write the number.

1 ⬭ + ⬭

2 5p – 2p   [p]

3 9 – 6

4 5 – 5

5 Add 6 and 6

6 Subtract 4 from 8

7 5 + 6

8 1p 5p 5p – 10p   [p]

9 The total of 6 and 4 is

10 2p + 2p + 2p   [p]

11 10p ÷ 2   [p]

12 7 sets of 2 are

13 Half of 16 is

14 Draw beads on the abacus to show 13

T   U

ANSWER

15 You have 12p. You spend 3p. How much do you have now?   [p]

16 14 + 16

17 5 × 10

18 60 ÷ 10

19 70 shared among 10 is

20 25 add 2 tens

21 55 – 40

22 Add 20 g and 70 g.   [g]

23 Write the number shown on the abacus.

H   T   U

24 80 + 100

25 140 – 100

26 10 tens are 7 tens more than

27 5p 5p 5p 5p

Write the total.   [p]

28 25 ÷ 5

29 7 sets of 5 are

30 9 × 5

Schofield & Sims Mental Arithmetic
Diagnostic check for Mental Arithmetic 1

Name:	
Class/Set:	Date:

ANSWER

1 Draw beads on the abacus to show 15

2 ■ + 7 = 10

3 19 – 4 – 7

4 What number is added to 6 to make 13?

5 5p + 10p + 20p = ___ p

6 Which two coins total 52p? ___ p + ___ p

7 £2 + £1 + 50p + 20p + 20p + 5p = £ ___

8 How many 10p coins have the same value as five 20p coins?

9 $\frac{1}{2} + \frac{1}{4}$

10 Write 11 quarters as a whole number and a fraction.

11 $\frac{1}{3}$ of a sum of money is 15p. How much is $\frac{2}{3}$ of the money? ___ p

12 $\frac{1}{10}$ of 50p = ___ p

13 A piece of wood is 23 cm long. How many centimetres are cut off to leave 19 cm? ___ cm

14 24 kg — A   8 kg — B

How much heavier is bag A than bag B? ___ kg

15 Song leaves home at 9.30 a.m. She arrives at her aunt's house at 10.53 a.m. How long has the journey taken? ___ hour ___ minutes

ANSWER

16 Castleham   Petershill   27 km   Markham

The total distance from Markham to Petershill is 52 km. How far is it from Castleham to Petershill? ___ km

17 9 × 2

18 30 ÷ ■ = 6

19 What number when multiplied by 3 will give a product of 30?

20 (6 × 3) + 4

21 What fraction is shaded?

22 A square has ■ right angles.

23 All the sides of this triangle are equal in length. What is the distance all the way round this triangle? 11 cm ___ cm

24 $9\frac{1}{2}$ cm   23 cm

By how many centimetres is the length of the rectangle greater than its width? ___ cm

25 800 + 70

26 Which of these numbers will divide exactly by 10 without a remainder? 45, 92, 150, 275

27 By how many metres is 1 km 300 m less than 2 km? ___ m

28 40p + 50p = £1 – ■ p ___ p

29 740 – 60

30 Jon bought $2\frac{1}{2}$ kg of carrots at 30p per $\frac{1}{2}$ kg. How much more than £1 did he spend? ___ p

From: **Mental Arithmetic Teacher's Guide** by Ann Montague-Smith (ISBN 978 07217 1211 6). Copyright © Schofield & Sims Ltd, 2013. Published by Schofield & Sims Ltd, Dogley Mill, Fenay Bridge, Huddersfield HD8 0NQ, UK (www.schofieldandsims.co.uk). **This page may be photocopied after purchase for use within your school or institution only.**

Schofield & Sims Mental Arithmetic
Diagnostic check for Mental Arithmetic 2

Name:

Class/Set: | Date:

ANSWER | ANSWER

1 Write 964 to the nearest 100

2 Write in figures seven hundred and eight.

3 How many hundreds in 4000?

4 35 + 18

5 What is the difference between 17 and 46?

6

DARTS SCORES	
Jan	**Sam**
21	19
15	17
18	16

How many more did Jan score than Sam?

7 How many more is 1020 minus 100 than 1200 minus 300?

8 $7 \times 4 = \blacksquare \times 7$

9 $(9 \times 6) + 7$

10 Divide 38 by 4 — rem.

11 Share 48 marbles equally between 5 children. How many will each child have? — rem.

12 $4\frac{1}{2} + 5\frac{1}{2} + 8$

13 $2 - \frac{1}{10}$

14 $3\frac{1}{2}$ kg × 3 — kg

15 4 litres 400 mℓ + $\frac{1}{2}$ litre — ℓ   mℓ

16 $\frac{7}{8} - \frac{1}{4}$

17 How many packs of nuts each containing 250 g can be filled from a box containing $5\frac{1}{2}$ kg?

18 30p + 6p – 7p — p

19 What remains when 50p is divided by 6? — p

20 What is the total of £2.55 and £3.75? — £

21 What will 8 apples cost if 10 apples cost £4.00? — £

22

Write to the nearest centimetre the length of line AB. — cm

23 Find the difference between 380 g and $\frac{1}{2}$ kg. — g

24 1750 mℓ, 350 mℓ and 600 mℓ are poured into a jug which will hold 3 litres. How much more will the jug hold? — mℓ

25

Afternoon

This clock is 15 minutes fast. Write the correct time. Use a.m. or p.m.

26 How many minutes from 11.45 a.m. to 12.20 p.m.? — min

27 How many days are there altogether in February and March in a leap year?

28

Which of these shapes is a triangle?

29

Which of these angles is an obtuse angle?

30 The total length of the sides of the triangle is 6 cm. What is the length of the side AB?

mm

From: **Mental Arithmetic Teacher's Guide** by Ann Montague-Smith (ISBN 978 07217 1211 6). Copyright © Schofield & Sims Ltd, 2013. Published by Schofield & Sims Ltd, Dogley Mill, Fenay Bridge, Huddersfield HD8 0NQ, UK (www.schofieldandsims.co.uk). **This page may be photocopied after purchase for use within your school or institution only.**

Schofield & Sims Mental Arithmetic

Diagnostic check for Mental Arithmetic 3

Name:	
Class/Set:	Date:

ANSWER

1 Write in numbers three thousand and eighty-four.

2 Look at the hundreds digit in this number: 6407 How many hundreds does this represent?

3 2300 + 700

4 25 + 9 + 17

5

SCORE CARD	
Tim	7
Mandeep	■
Kiri	8
Alexis	9

The total score was 28. What was Mandeep's score?

6 Dan had 60 marbles. He lost 23 and then won 17. How many marbles did he have then?

7 (8 × 6) + (6 × 8)

8 63 ÷ 7

9 Find the difference between 90 multiplied by 10 and 90 divided by 10

10 Add 10^2 to 9^2

11 $\frac{3}{4}$ = ■ eighths

12 Write $\frac{7}{10} + \frac{9}{100}$ as a decimal fraction.

13 Find $\frac{1}{2}$ of $3\frac{1}{2}$

14 32 × 5p coins = ■ 20p coins

15 £1 – thirty-two 2p coins   p

16 Oranges cost £2.60 per kg. What is the cost of 2 kg 500 g of oranges?   £

17

The scale shows the mass of a bag of sweets. How much will it cost at 40p per 100 g?   £

18 Write 45 cm as a decimal fraction of a metre.   m

19

Bottle A holds half as much as bottle B. Write the amount that bottle A holds in ℓ and mℓ. ℓ mℓ

ANSWER

20

Afternoon

This clock is 13 minutes fast. What is the correct time? Use a.m. or p.m.

21

Evening

Write the time shown on this clock using 24-hour clock time.

22

TIMETABLE		
	LEAVE HOLDEN	ARRIVE BADLEY
A	15.30	15.58
B	16.00	16.28
C	16.30	16.58

Which bus do I catch to arrive at Badley at 4.28 p.m.?

23 A girl faces North. She turns right until she faces West. Through how many right angles does she turn?

24

All the angles at the centre of the circle are equal How many degrees are there in the marked angle?   °

25

Find the measurement of angle Z in degrees.   °

26

Write the letter of the shape which is a rhombus.

27 A square has a perimeter of 72 m. How long is one side in metres?   m

28 A rectangular garden lawn has a long side of 12 m and a short side of 15 m. What is its perimeter in metres?   m

29 Mr Gupta walks around his square garden four times each day. Each side of his garden measures 35 m. How far does he walk in total?   m

30 A square piece of paper measures 10 cm along each side. What is its area in cm²?   cm²

Schofield & Sims Mental Arithmetic
Diagnostic check for Mental Arithmetic 4

Name:

Class/Set: 　　　　　　　　　　　　　　　　Date:

ANSWER

1 Write in words the number shown on the abacus picture.

Th H T U

2 $5^2 + 2^2 + 3^2$

3 $10^3 = \blacksquare \times \blacksquare \times \blacksquare = \blacksquare$

4 $\frac{9}{10}$ of 100 mℓ　　　　mℓ

5 19 quarters = $\blacksquare \frac{\blacksquare}{\blacksquare}$

6 $\frac{3}{5} = \frac{\blacksquare}{100}$　　　　$\overline{100}$

7 A jug when $\frac{7}{8}$ full holds 875 mℓ. How much does it hold when it is $\frac{3}{4}$ full?　　mℓ

8 $\frac{13}{20} = \frac{\blacksquare}{100} = \blacksquare$ %　　$\overline{100} = \quad$ %

9 10% of 620

10 20% of £35　　　£

11 Find the cost of 9 apples at 15p each.　　£

12 By how many pennies is 8 ten pence coins greater than 9 five pence coins and 1 two pence coin?　　p

13 How much does 80 cm of ribbon cost at £2.30 per m?　　£

14 Fuel costs £1.46 per litre. How much does 25 litres cost?　　£

15 $\frac{1}{4}$ kg − $\blacksquare$ g = 127 g　　g

16 A train travels at 80 km/h. How far will it go in 45 minutes?　　km

17 The total mass of 6 parcels is 4 kg 830 g. What is the average mass of the parcels?　　g

18 Write to the nearest metre: 18.53 m.　　m

19 Write six thousand two hundred and thirty-six to the nearest hundred in figures.

20 Jess bought 6 tennis balls at £2.79 each. How much did the balls cost to the nearest £?　　£

ANSWER

21 How many days were there in February 2008?

22 A bus runs every 15 minutes. If the first bus leaves at 08.20 at what time does the fifth bus leave?

23 How many days are there in total in August, September and October?

24 How many degrees are there in angle A?

55°　　A　　25°　　°

25 This shape has equal sides. How many degrees are there in ∠ A?

A　　°

26 In this right-angled triangle, what is the size in degrees of ∠ A?

A　　135°　　°

27 Find the area of:

15 cm

10 cm

8 cm

(a) the rectangle　　(a)　　cm²

(b) the triangle.　　(b)　　cm²

28 A box is 12 cm in length and 8 cm in width. How many centimetre cubes will fit exactly into the bottom of the box?

29 A box is 10 cm in length, 5 cm in width and 3 cm high. How many centimetre cubes will fit exactly into the box?

30 What is the volume of a box that is 12 cm long, 8 cm in width and 6 cm high?　　cm³

From: **Mental Arithmetic Teacher's Guide** by Ann Montague-Smith (ISBN 978 07217 1211 6). Copyright © Schofield & Sims Ltd, 2013. Published by Schofield & Sims Ltd, Dogley Mill, Fenay Bridge, Huddersfield HD8 0NQ, UK (www.schofieldandsims.co.uk). **This page may be photocopied after purchase for use within your school or institution only.**

Schofield & Sims Mental Arithmetic
Diagnostic check for Mental Arithmetic 5

Name:	
Class/Set:	Date:

ANSWER

1 $70\,000 + 4000 + 30 + 5$

2 $(8 \times 10^3) + (6 \times 10^2)$

3 $(8 \times 10^6) + (3 \times 10^4) + (5 \times 10^2)$

4 $7\frac{3}{5} = \frac{\blacksquare}{5}$ — $\frac{}{5}$

5 $2\frac{3}{4}$ kg – ■ g = 2.1 kg — g

6 $\frac{3}{5}$ of 1.6 kg = ■ g — g

7 What percentage of 1 km is 450 m? — %

8 70% of £9.90 — £

9 Jan's aunt gives her £3.60. She decides to save 15% of this. How much does she save? — £

10 Sally spent $\frac{1}{5}$ of £6 on crisps, and $\frac{1}{4}$ of the remainder on sweets. How much money is left? — £

11 What is the annual interest on £750 at 4%? — £

12 £1.20 was received in change from £10 after buying 8 plants. Find the average cost of a plant. — £

13 6 articles cost £9.57. Find the cost of one article to the nearest penny. — £

14 640 min = ■ h ■ min — h   min

15 How many days in 29 weeks?

16 A car travels 27.4 km in 15 min. Find its speed in km/h. — km/h

17 Find in degrees the difference between the temperatures 8 °C and –6 °C. — °C

18

cm	1	2	3	4	5	6
	5	10	15	20	25	30
km						

The scale is taken from a map. Find the distance in kilometres represented by a line measuring 5.4 cm. — km

19 A notebook is 1.9 cm thick. What would be the height of a pile of 12 notebooks? — cm

ANSWER

20 Approximate 389607 to the nearest 1000.

21 Divide £20 by 6. Give the answer to the nearest penny. — £

22 Paul earns £845.76 a month. Approximate this amount to the nearest £10 and then find his approximate annual salary. — £

23 Calculate the size of the reflex angle AOC. — °

(angles: 95°, 46° at O, with points A, B, C)

24 Estimate the bearing of the point B from A. — °

(grid with North arrow, points A and B)

25 Find the circumference of the circle to the nearest centimetre. ($C = 2\pi r$; $\pi = 3.14$) — cm

(circle with radius 1.2 cm)

26 Find in degrees ∠BCD. — °

(trapezium with angles 125° at A and 125° at B, points A, B, C, D)

27 ∠b is $\frac{1}{3}$ the size of ∠c. What is the size of ∠a? — °

(angles a, b, c)

28 A box is 24 cm long, 6 cm wide and 6 cm deep. Find its volume. — cm³

29 The volume of a cuboid is 144 cm³ and the area of one of its faces is 16 cm². Find its length. — cm

30 A circle has a radius of 2 m. Find its area. (Area of a circle = πr^2, $\pi = 3.14$) — m²

From: **Mental Arithmetic Teacher's Guide** by Ann Montague-Smith (ISBN 978 07217 1211 6). Copyright © Schofield & Sims Ltd, 2013. Published by Schofield & Sims Ltd, Dogley Mill, Fenay Bridge, Huddersfield HD8 0NQ, UK (www.schofieldandsims.co.uk). **This page may be photocopied after purchase for use within your school or institution only.**

Schofield & Sims Mental Arithmetic

Diagnostic check for Mental Arithmetic 6

Name:

Class/Set: Date:

ANSWER

ANSWER

1 66% is larger than $\frac{2}{3}$.
True or false?

2 Approximate 9501 to the
nearest hundred.

3 2.6×10^4

4 A recipe asks for 3 parts butter to
5 parts sugar. If the total mass of
the butter in the recipe is 510 g,
how much will the total mass of
the sugar be in kilograms?

kg

5 Write the two missing
terms in this sequence.
$1, \frac{1}{2}, \blacksquare, \blacksquare, \frac{1}{16}$

and

6 Write $\frac{2}{5}$ of 9.5 as a decimal.

7 I buy a TV for £450 and pay
in 8 equal instalments.
How much is each instalment?

£

8 $6\frac{1}{2}$ lb is approximately $\blacksquare$ kg.

kg

9 $8 < \sqrt{80} < 10$. True or false?

10 $13 \div 0.13$

11 £16.48 − 236p

£

12 How many Swedish Krona
will you get for £30 at
11 Krona to £1?

Krona

13 If 6 articles cost 90p,
what will 50 articles cost?

£

14 Share £6.42 in
the ratio 1:2.

£   :   £

15 If $d = 6$ and $e = 2$, find the
value of $\frac{de}{d+e}$.

16 If $g = 4$ and $h = 6$,
evaluate $g^2 + h$.

17 Express 18 as a product
of prime numbers by
filling in the blanks.

$3 \times$ $\times$

18 $3x + 18 = 0$ so $x = \blacksquare$

19 5 h 25 min = $\blacksquare$ min

min

20 Oil flowing in a pipe takes
20 s to travel 32 cm.
Find its speed in mm/s.

mm/s

21 How many hours and
minutes are there from
8.30 p.m. Monday to
10.13 a.m. Tuesday?

h   min

22 What is my speed if I
travel $\frac{1}{4}$ mile in 3 minutes?

mph

23 The smallest angle of a
parallelogram is 45°.
What size is the largest angle?

°

24 Find the area of a circle whose
radius is 5 cm. ($A = \pi r^2$, $\pi = 3.14$)

cm²

25

Write down the length of side x.

cm

26

For the trapezium shown, write
down the sizes of angles x and y.

$x =$ °

$y =$ °

27 Three TV programmes last for
15 min, 45 min and 1 h 55 min
respectively. What is the total
length of all three programmes
to the nearest hour?

h

28 Approximate 64 ft to the
nearest yard.

yd

29 A tank of water is 420 cm long,
215 cm wide, and 85 cm deep.
Find its approximate volume to
the nearest cubic metre.

m³

30 Express 499 seconds to the
nearest minute.

min

Marking key to the Diagnostic check for Mental Arithmetic Introductory Book

Use the **Activity prompts** to help pupils overcome problems with particular question types.
Other activities may be developed from these prompts.

Adding and subtracting to 10

1 6   **2** 3p   **3** 3

> **Activity prompt:** Suggest to pupils that they use a mental number line. Say, for 3 + 5: *Put the larger number in your head on the number line. Now count on three: so 5 and 6, 7, 8. 3 add 5 equals 8.* For subtraction pupils can count up from the smaller to the larger number. So, for 5 − 3: *Begin on 3. Now count on up to 5. That is 3 and 4, 5. So 5 subtract 3 is 2.* To begin with pupils may find it helpful to use their fingers to keep track of how many they count.

Doubles

4 0   **5** 12   **6** 4

> **Activity prompt:** Ask pupils to make towers of cubes to show doubles. For example, for double 5 they make two towers of five cubes then combine them to make the double. When they are confident with this, ask them to count on mentally from one number to the second. For example, double 5 is: *5 and 6, 7, 8, 9, 10. So double 5 is 10.*

Near doubles

7 11   **8** 1p   **9** 10

> **Activity prompt:** Ask pupils to look carefully at the two numbers and decide which is the nearest double fact that they could use. So for 5 + 6 they look for double 5 add 1. For 8 + 6 they look for double 6 add 2, and so on. They can use mental number lines to count on if they do not yet know the double facts.

Multiplication and division by 2

10 6p   **11** 5p   **12** 14   **13** 8

> **Activity prompt:** Count together in twos, starting from zero to 20, then back again to zero. When pupils are confident with this, ask them to count in twos to find 4 multiplied by 2, 5 multiplied by 2, and so on. Then ask them to use counting back in twos to find 14 shared among 2. They use their fingers to keep track of how many twos they count. Repeat for more multiplication and division examples for 2.

Adding and subtracting to 20

14   **15** 9p   **16** 30

Activity prompt: Use a two-spike abacus and beads and ask pupils to show you some numbers from 11 to 20, such as 12, 15, 17 … Check that pupils understand what each digit in the number stands for; for example, that 12 is 1 ten and 2 units. Now provide some examples of addition with answers between 11 and 20, such as 6 + 8 and 9 + 7. Check that pupils use a mental number line and count on from the larger number if they do not have recall of the answer. For subtraction pupils can count up from the smaller number to find the difference: so for 15 – 8, they count *8 and 9, 10, 11, 12, 13, 14, 15. So 15 subtract 8 is 7.* Allow them to keep track of how many numbers they count by using their fingers.

Multiplication and division by 10

17 50   **18** 6   **19** 7

Activity prompt: Count in tens from zero to 100 then back to zero. Now ask pupils to find answers by counting up or back in tens; for example, *What is 6 multiplied by 10?* Pupils count up in tens, from zero, for 6 tens. They count back in tens to find, for example, 70 divided by 10. If necessary, ask pupils to keep track of the count with their fingers, until they are confident with this.

Addition and subtraction of tens

20 45   **21** 15   **22** 90 g

Activity prompt: Ask pupils to start on, say, 15, and add three tens, perhaps using copymaster 'Counting square'. Say: *15 and 10 is 25, and 10 is 35 and 10 is 45. So 15 add three tens is 45.* Repeat, counting back the required number of tens for subtraction; for example, 61 subtract 30: *61, 51, 41, 31.*

Addition and subtraction of tens and hundreds

23 425   **24** 180   **25** 40   **26** 3 tens *or* 30

Activity prompt: Use a three-spike abacus to check that pupils can read and write three-digit numbers. Ask, for 523: *What does the 5 … 2 … 3 stand for?* Model some addition and subtraction examples using the abacus to show what happens when a hundred is added or removed, such as 210 add 100 or 210 subtract 100.

Multiplication and division by 5

27 20p   **28** 5   **29** 35   **30** 45

Activity prompt: Practise counting in fives from zero to 50 and back again. Now ask pupils to find answers to multiplication questions such as 6 × 5. They count from zero in fives six times to reach 30. Repeat, counting back in fives, to find 30 ÷ 5.

Marking key to the Diagnostic check for Mental Arithmetic 1

Use the **Activity prompts** to help pupils overcome problems with particular question types.
Other activities may be developed from these prompts.

Number facts to 20

1   **2** 3 **3** 8 **4** 7

Activity prompts:

Place value: Provide a two-spike abacus and beads, and ask pupils to place beads on the spikes to represent the numbers that you say, such as *15, 23, 38* … Ask, for example, for 23: *What do the two beads represent? What do the three beads represent? What number is this?*

Addition and subtraction: Ask pupils to use a mental number line, counting up from the larger number for addition, and up from the smaller number for subtraction (to find the difference).

Money

5 35p **6** 50p + 2p **7** £3.95 **8** 10

Activity prompts:

Coin recognition: If pupils are unsure about the value of coins, ask them to match pennies to 2p, 5p and 10p coins for equivalence. Repeat this with other equivalences such as 2p, 2p and 1p for 5p. Repeat this over time for larger value coins. The shapes of coins to £1 are shown on copymaster 'Units of measurement – and money'.

Addition of money: Provide coins for pupils to match to what is to be added or subtracted. Encourage them to count on to find totals.

Fractions

9 $\frac{3}{4}$ **10** $2\frac{3}{4}$ **11** 30p **12** 5p

Activity prompts:

Fractions of quantities: Provide copymaster 'Fractions chart' and resources so that pupils can model the problem. For example, ask a pupil to cut three paper squares into quarters. Ask him or her to count out eleven quarters, then see how many squares he or she can make and what fraction of a square is left over.

Money fractions: Provide coins so that pupils can model the problem, for example changing a 50p coin into smaller, equal coins (e.g. 5p coins) so that they can find $\frac{1}{10}$ of the amount.

Measures

13   4 cm   **14**   16 kg   **15**   1 hour and 23 minutes   **16**   25 km

Activity prompts:

Length and weight: Ask pupils to say what sort of problem it is, such as addition or subtraction. Ask them to use a mental number line in order to count up to find the solution. If they find this difficult, provide a numbered number line, such as copymaster 'Number line: 0 to 100', for them to use until they are confident with this method.

Time: Provide a clock face that pupils can use to model the problem. Provide simpler problems to begin with, such as finding the length of time between 5 p.m. and 5.20 p.m.; then 5.25 p.m. and 5.50 p.m.; then times which cross the hour, such as 5.55 p.m. and 6.10 p.m.

Multiplication facts

17   18   **18**   5   **19**   10   **20**   22

Activity prompts:

Multiplication table facts: Practise reciting table facts for the 2, 5 and 10 times tables. Then ask pupils to recall specific facts, such as 5×2 or 9×10. When pupils are confident with these, repeat with facts for the 3 and 6 times tables. Ask pupils to give two related facts such as $8 \times 3 = 24$ and $24 \div 3 = 8$. You might want to use copymaster 'Multiplication square'.

Word problems: Check that pupils understand the mathematical vocabulary used. For example, for a question using the word 'product', ask pupils to give their own multiplication problem using the word to demonstrate that they understand its meaning.

Shape

21 $\frac{1}{5}$ **22**   4   **23**   33 cm   **24** $13\frac{1}{2}$ cm

Activity prompts:

Shape recognition: Provide some shape tiles of regular shapes (for example, a square, rectangle and pentagon), and ask pupils to name each one's properties. Then ask them to sketch examples of each of these shapes to demonstrate that they understand what is specific about each one. You might want to display 'Two-dimensional (2-D) shapes and three-dimensional (3-D) shapes'.

Shape word problems: These problems involve shapes and numbers. Ask pupils to say in their own words what the problem is asking and what mathematical operation is needed to solve it. If necessary, provide smaller numbers for similar problems until pupils are confident.

Numbers to 999

25   870   **27**   700 m   **29**   680

26   150   **28**   10p   **30**   50p

Activity prompts:

Hundreds and tens: Encourage pupils to add on in tens to hundreds by counting. Similarly they can count back in tens if they are not sure about an example such as $740 - 60$.

Word problems: Ask pupils to explain the problem in their own words and to say which operation is needed. Ask them to find key words in the problem that point to the operation, such as 'less' and 'more'. If necessary, provide smaller numbers with similar words so that pupils gain confidence in answering such problems.

Marking key to the Diagnostic check for Mental Arithmetic 2

Use the **Activity prompts** to help pupils overcome problems with particular question types.
Other activities may be developed from these prompts.

Numbers to 1000

1 1000   **2** 708   **3** 40

Activity prompt: Draw a four-spike abacus and provide some counters. Ask pupils to set out counters for the numbers that you say. Begin with tens and units numbers such as 85, 97, and so on. Extend to hundreds in the same way, then thousands. Ask questions such as: *How many units/tens/hundreds/thousands are there in this number? How do you know that?*

Addition and subtraction

4 53   **5** 29   **6** 2   **7** 20

Activity prompt: Use copymaster 'Number line: 0 to 100'. For 35 + 18:

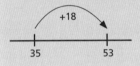

Discuss how 35 + 18 is the same as 35 + 10 + 8. For difference use a similar method, counting up from the smaller to the larger number. Repeat the method for larger numbers.

Multiplication and division facts for the 2, 3, 4, 5, 6 and 10 times tables

8 4   **9** 61   **10** 9 rem. 2   **11** 9 rem. 3

Activity prompt: If pupils are unsure of table facts, practise reciting the facts. Then ask questions related to the table. Check that pupils understand, for example, that 6 × 4 = 24, 4 × 6 = 24, 24 ÷ 6 = 4 and 24 ÷ 4 = 6 and that if one of these facts is known the others can be deduced. Model division with remainders using counters or cubes until pupils are able to calculate this for themselves by using table facts and finding the difference between the fact and the amount to be divided. You might want to use copymaster 'Multiplication square'.

Fractions

12 18   **13** $1\frac{9}{10}$ **14** $10\frac{1}{2}$ kg

Activity prompt: Provide copymaster 'Fractions chart' and suggest that pupils sketch simple diagrams on squared paper so that they can show the whole numbers and fractions. For example, for $2 - \frac{1}{10}$, they could use 10 squares to represent 1, 20 for 2, and can then subtract $\frac{1}{10}$.

Equivalence of fractions

15 4 ℓ 900 mℓ   **16** $\frac{5}{8}$ **17** 22

Activity prompt: Discuss fraction families, such as halves, quarters, eighths; fifths, tenths; and so on. Ask questions such as: *How many eighths are there in a quarter? How do you know that?* Now ask pupils to find $\frac{1}{4} - \frac{1}{8}$, then $\frac{3}{8} - \frac{1}{4}$, and so on. Pupils could colour in copymaster 'Fractions chart'.

Money

18 29p   **19** 2p   **20** £6.30   **21** £3.20

Activity prompt: Check pupils understand what, for example, £2.55 is in pounds and pence. Provide some coins and ask them to set out appropriate coins to answer the questions. For example, for 50p ÷ 6 they would need to think about the units of money that they would need to answer the question. Where the answer is found by addition, check that they use the largest denomination possible, and total the coins correctly. Repeat for working mentally.

Measures

22 6 cm   **23** 120 g   **24** 300 mℓ

Activity prompt: Check pupils use a ruler correctly, and understand where to begin and finish a measure. Ask them to give the equivalent value of, for example, 1750 mℓ in litres and mℓ. They can draw a large jug and use it like an empty number line, adding quantities, then mark what the total is each time.

Time

25 5.50 p.m.   **26** 35 min   **27** 60

Activity prompt: Check pupils can read a clock accurately, and transfer a time from analogue to digital form. Ask them to find the time 10 minutes before 3.05, and 10 minutes after 3.55, to check that they understand what happens to the hour time before and after the o'clock time. Check that they know how many days are in each month. Use the rhyme on copymaster 'Months of the year' to help them remember.

Shapes and angles

28 A   **29** C   **30** 24 mm

Activity prompt: Provide some shape tiles of regular shapes. Scatter these in front of pupils and ask them to name each one. Turn each shape so that it is in a different orientation, and repeat. Ask pupils to point to the shapes with right angles. Ask them to sketch a right angle, then an obtuse angle. Ask: *What is the difference between a right angle and an obtuse angle?*

Marking key to the Diagnostic check for Mental Arithmetic 3

Use the **Activity prompts** to help pupils overcome problems with particular question types.
Other activities may be developed from these prompts.

Place value

1 3084   **2** 4

> **Activity prompt:** Shuffle two sets of 0–9 numeral cards. Ask a pupil to take the top three cards and use them to make a three-digit number. Ask him or her to read the number. Then ask, for example: *Which digit shows how many hundreds … tens … units there are?* Repeat this for further examples, then extend to four-digit numbers.

Addition and subtraction

3 3000   **4** 51   **5** 4   **6** 54

> **Activity prompt:** Discuss with pupils how they would solve the addition or subtraction. For addition, encourage them to total the tens mentally, then the units. For subtraction, they can use an empty number line, such as copymaster 'Number line: 0 to 100', and count up from the smaller to the larger number.

Multiplication and division

7 96   **8** 9   **9** 891   **10** 181

> **Activity prompt:** Ask, for example: *What is 6 multiplied by 7?* Now ask for three other facts that use the same numbers: 7 × 6 = 42; 42 ÷ 7 = 6; and 42 ÷ 6 = 7. Repeat this for other facts, choosing those that are often forgotten, such as 7 × 7; 8 × 6; 8 × 7; 9 × 6; 9 × 7; 9 × 8; 9 × 9. Discuss how if one fact is known then the other three can be deduced. You might want to use copymaster 'Multiplication square'.

Fractions

11 6   **12** 0.79   **13** $1\frac{3}{4}$

> **Activity prompt:** Check pupils understand what the denominator of a fraction refers to. Use copymaster 'Fractions chart' or, for example, draw a rectangle of eight squares. Ask: *What does one square represent? So what do two squares represent? Tell me another way that we can express* $\frac{2}{8}$. Agree that this is the same as $\frac{1}{4}$. Repeat for other equivalences such as $\frac{4}{8}$ and $\frac{1}{2}$; and $\frac{6}{8}$ and $\frac{3}{4}$. Repeat for a rectangle which has 10 squares; then 12 squares.

Money

14 8 **15** 36p **16** £6.50

Activity prompt: Model the questions using coins. Pupils count out the appropriate coins and use these to help them to calculate. For example, for thirty-two 2p coins, ask the pupils to count out the 32 coins and then exchange these for others until they have the least possible number of coins: 50p, 10p and two 2p coins.

Measures

17 £1.40 **18** 0.45 m **19** 1 ℓ 400 mℓ

Activity prompt: Provide some measuring equipment such as a metre stick marked in cm; a scale marked in 100 g increments; and a jug marked in 100 mℓ increments. Pupils use these to make measurements and to demonstrate that they understand how to read the scales. Check that they understand 'in between' readings, such as between 100 g and 200 g.

Time

20 4.52 p.m. **21** 23.00 **22** B

Activity prompt: Write some times using 24-hour clock time. Ask pupils to say the time. Now ask: *Is this morning or afternoon? How do you know that? Tell me this time in 12-hour time.* Discuss how 24-hour clock time is used for timetables in order to avoid confusion about a.m. and p.m. times.

Angles and shapes

23 3 **24** 60° **25** 50° **26** B

Activity prompt: Check pupils understand what a right angle is, then ask them to stand, and turn to North (or, say, the door) then turn a right angle left, right, and so on. Now ask them to choose from a set of shape tiles all the shapes they can see which have right angles. Now ask them to point to all the angles they see which are not right angles. Discuss the fact that a right angle measures 90°.

Perimeter and area

27 18 m **28** 54 m **29** 560 m **30** 100 cm²

Activity prompt: Provide squared paper and ask pupils to draw a rectangle three squares by four squares. Now ask them to find its perimeter. If they count the squares, ask them to look at the opposite sides and agree that these are equal in length. Ask them to calculate the perimeter by adding the two multiples ($\ell \times 2$ and $b \times 2$). Repeat this for the area, which they may calculate by counting squares. Point out that this gives the same answer as multiplying the two sides together ($\ell \times b$). You might want to display copymasters 'Perimeter' and 'Area'.

Marking key to the Diagnostic check for Mental Arithmetic 4

Use the **Activity prompts** to help pupils overcome problems with particular question types.
Other activities may be developed from these prompts.

Number

1 Five thousand, two hundred and four

> **Activity prompt:** Ask pupils to draw some three-spike abacuses. Now ask them to draw beads on the abacuses to show, for example: 356, 450, 603. Ask pupils to explain what each spike represents and to explain the empty spikes. Repeat this for four-spike abacuses, with numbers such as 4567, 2308, 3089, and so on.

2 38   **3** (10 × 10 × 10 =) 1000

> **Activity prompt:** Check pupils understand what, for example, 2^2 represents. Repeat this for other square numbers, such as 4^2. Ask pupils to write down 4 × 4. When pupils are confident with square numbers, ask them to total two square numbers, then three. Repeat this for cube numbers, including 10^3.

Fractions

4 90 ml   **5** $4\frac{3}{4}$ **6** $\frac{60}{100}$ **7** 750 ml

> **Activity prompt:** Provide a jug marked in 100 ml increments to 1 litre. Ask pupils to say how many ml, $\frac{1}{2}$, $\frac{1}{4}$, $\frac{1}{5}$, $\frac{3}{4}$, $\frac{3}{8}$ of a litre, and so on, would be. Check that they understand how to calculate these fractions of a litre.

Percentages

8 $\frac{65}{100}$ = 65%   **9** 62   **10** £7

> **Activity prompt:** Ask pupils to find equivalent percentages for fractions such as $\frac{1}{2}$, $\frac{1}{4}$, $\frac{3}{4}$. Now ask them to find percentages of given amounts, such as 1%, 10%, 50%, and so on. Ask them to explain how they calculated the answer. You might want to use copymaster 'Fraction equivalencies'.

Money

11 £1.35   **12** 33p   **13** £1.84   **14** £36.50

> **Activity prompt:** Provide coins and notes so that pupils can model the calculations. Then ask them to explain how they calculated the answer. Ask them to find the key words in the question that help them to decide what calculation they need to carry out.

Measures

15   123 g   **16**   60 km   **17**   805 g

Activity prompt: Ask pupils to read each question carefully and then explain what calculation is required. Ask them to find the words or symbols that have helped them. If necessary, simplify the size of the numbers involved so that pupils can practise answering word problems about measures. Then ask them to try these questions again.

Approximations

18   19 m   **19**   6200   **20**   £17

Activity prompt: Ask pupils to give some approximations, such as: *What is 6509 to the nearest ten, hundred, thousand?* Ask them to explain or justify their answer.

Time

21   29   **22**   09.20   **23**   92

Activity prompt: Ask pupils to explain how to decide if a year is a leap year and how that affects the month of February. Review the months of the year and how many days are in each month, using copymaster 'Months of the year'. Provide a clock face and, for question 22, ask pupils to show at what time each bus leaves.

Shapes and angles

24   100°   **25**   60°   **26**   45°

Activity prompt: Revise total degrees of angles in a triangle (180°), total degrees of two angles on a straight line (180°), and total degrees of angles around a point (360°). Now ask pupils to calculate the remaining angle in a right-angled triangle, if the second angle is 30°.

Area and volume

27   (a) 150 cm²   (b) 35 cm²   **29**   150

28   96   **30**   576 cm³

Activity prompt: Ask pupils to find the areas of rectangles. They can draw the rectangles on squared paper, then count squares. Review with pupils how the count is equivalent to the result when the length and breadth are multiplied together, perhaps referring to copymaster 'Area'. Repeat this for volume. Begin with cubes in boxes, or by building cubes and cuboids with cubes. Pupils count the cubes, and notice that the result when the length, breadth and height are multiplied together gives the same result.

Marking key to the Diagnostic check for Mental Arithmetic 5

Use the **Activity prompts** to help pupils overcome problems with particular question types.
Other activities may be developed from these prompts.

Number

1 74 035 **2** 8600 **3** 8 030 500

Activity prompt: If pupils are unsure about these powers of 10, ask them to write out the multiplication. For example, $10^6 = 10 \times 10 \times 10 \times 10 \times 10 \times 10 = 1\,000\,000$. Pupils may find it helpful to model their answers on a seven-spike paper abacus. Ask them to read their answers aloud.

Fractions and decimal fractions

4 $\frac{38}{5}$ **5** 650 g **6** 960 g

Activity prompt: Provide opportunities for pupils to convert fractions to decimals and vice versa. For example, ask: *What is $\frac{3}{4}$ as a decimal fraction? How did you calculate that? Now what is $1\frac{1}{2}$ kg as a decimal fraction of a kilogram? And how many grams is that?* You might want to use copymaster 'Fraction equivalencies'.

Percentages

7 45% **8** £6.93 **9** £0.54

Activity prompt: Check with pupils the strategy and method they use to find a percentage of a quantity. Give some simple examples, such as 25% of £16. Increase the complexity of the examples once pupils are confident with the method.

Money

10 £3.60 **11** £30 **12** £1.10 **13** £1.60

Activity prompt: Provide simpler questions which involve division of money; for example, ask: *What is $\frac{1}{5}$ of £2.60? What is 20% of £8? If 3 plants cost £2.40, find the average price of one plant.* Check pupils' method for efficiency and accuracy.

Time

14 10 h 40 min **15** 203 **16** 109.6 km/h

Activity prompt: Revise the units of time: the number of days in a week, minutes in an hour, and so on, perhaps using copymaster 'Time'. Then refer back to questions 14 and 15 and ask pupils to find the words or symbols that suggest what operation they need to carry out. For speed, discuss the question, and what clues there are in the question.

Measures

17 14 °C   **18** 27 km   **19** 22.8 cm

> **Activity prompt:** For temperature provide a thermometer marked in °C from −10 °C to +10 °C. Give examples of differences in temperature, such as the difference between −4 °C and 5 °C. Check pupils can read the scale of a map accurately and understand what the millimetre marks between each centimetre mark represent.

Approximations

20 390 000   **21** £3.33   **22** £10 200

> **Activity prompt:** Ask similar questions, using the same words but much simpler numbers. For example: *Approximate 389 to the nearest 100.* Ask pupils what they need to do in order to find the answer, and which words in the question give the clue. For question 22, ask, for example: *Paul gets £15.60 pocket money a month. Approximate this amount to the nearest pound. Now find his approximate annual pocket money.*

Angles

23 219°   **24** 225°   **25** 8 cm

> **Activity prompt:** Provide a compass and ask pupils to point it to North. Now ask them to calculate how many degrees they will turn through if they turn from North to East, then South, then West, each time starting from North.

Shapes

26 55°   **27** 120°

> **Activity prompt:** Review total degrees of angles in a quadrilateral (360°), the properties of a trapezium, total degrees of angles around a point (360°), and total degrees of angles on a straight line (180°).

Area and volume

28 864 cm³   **29** 9 cm   **30** 12.56 m²

> **Activity prompt:** Ask pupils to sketch a simple diagram for each question and mark in what is known. Now ask them to decide on what mathematics to use to find the solution, and to explain their thinking.

Marking key to the Diagnostic check for Mental Arithmetic 6

Use the **Activity prompts** to help pupils overcome problems with particular question types.
Other activities may be developed from these prompts.

Number

1 False

2 9500

3 26 000

4 0.85 kg

5 $\frac{1}{4}$ and $\frac{1}{8}$

> **Activity prompt:** These questions call on pupils' understanding of number. Where pupils have difficulty, read the question with them and ask them to explain which is the important vocabulary and how they know that. Teach the concept again if necessary.

Computation

6 3.8

7 £56.25

8 3 kg

9 True

10 100

> **Activity prompt:** Pupils may find question 9 difficult. It involves a square root, but it is not necessary to find √80 in order to find the answer. Ask pupils to use their knowledge of square numbers to find one close to 80 (9 × 9 = 81). They will then see that √80 is more than 8 and less than 10.

Money

11 £14.12

12 330 Krona

13 £7.50

14 £2.14 : £4.28

> **Activity prompt:** Ask pupils to read each question aloud. Now ask them to say which are the key mathematical words that give clues as to how to tackle the problem. Then ask them to say whether this is a one-stage problem or whether two or more stages are needed to solve it, and how they would do this.

Algebra

15 1.5 *or* $1\frac{1}{2}$

16 22

17 3 × 3 × 2

18 −6

> **Activity prompt:** Ask questions such as: *What does de mean?* Check pupils understand the way in which algebraic notation is written. For example, *de = d × e*. Check pupils have strategies for solving equations, such as, in question 18, subtracting 18 from both sides of the equation.

Measures

19 325 min **20** 16 mm/s **21** 13 h 43 min **22** 5 mph

Activity prompt: Each of these questions relies on pupils understanding what mathematics they need to solve the question. Ask them to explain which vocabulary is important in making this decision. Ask pupils to answer questions about time such as: *How many minutes are there in one hour? How would you calculate how many minutes there are in a day ... a week ... a year? How would you calculate how many hours in 3240 minutes?*

Space and shape

23 135° **24** 78.5 cm² **25** 10 cm **26** $x = 110°, y = 150°$

Activity prompt: Check that pupils know how many degrees there are in total in a triangle and in any four-sided figure such as a rectangle, square or parallelogram. It may help pupils to measure the angles of a parallelogram with a protractor, then to total them. These questions rely on pupils' knowledge of the properties of shapes. Where pupils are unsure, ask them to sketch the shape and to state what they know about it. Ask questions such as: *Will all the angles in this shape be the same size? Why not? Which will be the same size? How do you know that?* Use copymaster 'Parts of a circle' to make sure pupils know what the radius is.

Approximations

27 3 h **28** 21 yd **29** 8 m³ **30** 8 min

Activity prompt: Discuss with pupils the rules for approximating. For example, 155 seconds is 2 minutes and 35 seconds, and approximates to 3 minutes because 35 seconds is more than half a minute. 132 seconds is 2 minutes and 12 seconds, and approximates to 2 minutes because 12 seconds is less than half a minute. The same rules apply for approximating other measures.

Schofield & Sims Mental Arithmetic

General resources

Use these resources as your pupils begin working through the **Mental Arithmetic** pupil books.

Every resource in this section may be photocopied after purchase for use within your school or institution only.

Entry test
Group record sheet

Schofield & Sims Mental Arithmetic

Class/Set	Teacher's name	Date of test

Pupil's name	Entry test total score	Schofield & Sims Mental Arithmetic book						
		IB	1	2	3	4	5	6

Total number of books required:

Entry test total score	Schofield & Sims Mental Arithmetic book	Number of pupil books required		Entry test total score	Schofield & Sims Mental Arithmetic book	Number of pupil books required
0–15	Introductory book (red)			51–70	Book 3 (light green)	
16–30	Book 1 (dark green)			71–90	Book 4 (dark blue/purple)	
31–50	Book 2 (blue)			91+	Book 5* (orange)	

*All those pupils who score more than 90 on the **Entry test** should be asked to work on Book 5 for at least a few weeks – so you can ensure that they are comfortable with all the concepts covered. Those whose high scores continue for a period of a few weeks or longer should be promoted to Book 6 (grey).

The language of maths: Introductory Book

+ is the plus sign, for 'add'

addition – 'counting up' or 'finding the sum of' two or more numbers. (3 add 3 = 6)

altogether – to find how many there are altogether, add them all up. (10 + 2 + 3 = 15. There are 15 altogether.)

greater than – here is an example: 4 greater than 5 = 9

increase – if something is increased you have more of it. Increase 3 by 2 and you get 5

more than – here is an example: '6 more than 3' is the same as '6 and 3 more'. (6 more than 3 = 9)

plus – means 'add'. (8 plus 8 = 16 *or* 8 + 8 = 16)

sum – to find the sum, add up all the numbers. (The sum of 2 and 4 = 6)

total – means 'count' or 'add'. (The total of 4, 2 and 3 = 9)

How many more than 3 is 5? Answer: 2

– is the minus sign, for 'subtract' or 'take away'

decrease – means 'make something less'. Decrease 3 by 2 and you get 1. You started with 3, you took 2 away, you have 1 left.

difference – to find the difference between numbers, compare them. There are two ways to find the difference between 8 and 3. Count on from the smaller number 3 to the larger number 8 or write down the larger amount and take the smaller amount away from it. The difference between 8 and 3 is 5

fewer than – means 'less than'. (3 fewer than 7 is 4)

less – means 'fewer than' or 'not as many'. (4 less than 5 is 1)

minus – means 'take away'. (8 minus 5 = 3 *or* 8 – 5 = 3)

subtraction – is 'taking away'. The answer is the number you have left. For example: We have 6 eggs. We subtract 2 so we take away 2. We have 4 left.

take away – here is an example: 6 take away 4 = 2. Sometimes this is written as 'take 4 from 6'. Write down the 6 first so that you can take 4 away from it. (6 – 4 = 2)

What is left when you take 2 from 4? Answer: 2

× is the multiplication sign, for 'multiply' or 'times'

multiplication – a quick way to add up equal sets.

multiply – here is an example: multiply 2 by 6 = 12. So 2 × 6 means '2 multiplied by 6' or '2 times 6'

product – your answer when something has been multiplied. (3 × 4 = 12 so the product of 3 and 4 is 12)

times – can mean 'multiplied by'. (4 times 2 is 8 *or* 4 × 2 = 8)

÷ is the division sign, for 'divide by'

dividing – splitting things into equal groups. (Divide 6 by 2 = 3. You have split 6 into 2 equal groups, with 3 in each. 6 ÷ 2 = 3)

share – another way of 'dividing' or 'splitting up'. For example, share 10 between 5 people and they get 2 each.

How many 2s in 8? Answer: 4

= is the equals sign

We use this sign instead of the words 'makes' or 'is the same as'. (You might say '5 add 3 = 8' *or* '5 add 3 is the same as 8' *or* '5 add 3 makes 8')

Fractions

half ($\frac{1}{2}$) – to find half of something we divide it by 2. We halve it. (Half of 10 is 5)

quarter ($\frac{1}{4}$) – divide something into four equal pieces, and each piece is called a quarter.

The language of maths: Book 1

a.m. – when written after a time (for example, '9 a.m.'), 'a.m.' stands for 'ante meridian', which is another way of saying 'before midday'. So '9 a.m.' means 'nine o'clock in the morning'.

brackets – if a question has some numbers in brackets, you should work out what is in the brackets before you do the rest of the question. For example, in the sum $(7 \times 4) + 3$ you would multiply 7×4 before trying to add 3 to it. Your answer would be 31.

double – twice. When you double something you make it twice as big. Doubling is the same as multiplying by 2 and so double 5 is 10 because $5 \times 2 = 10$.

dozen – 12. A dozen means 12, so 'I would like a dozen buns' means 'I would like 12 buns'.

estimate – a sensible guess.

even numbers – whole numbers that can be divided exactly by 2. For example:
8 divided by 2 = 4, so 8 is an even number.
9 divided by 2 = 4 with 1 left over, so 9 is not an even number: it is an **odd** number.
Even numbers always end in 0, 2, 4, 6 or 8.

fraction – a part of something. The bottom number of a fraction is called the denominator. It tells us the fraction's name and how many equal parts something has been divided into. The top number of a fraction is called the numerator. It tells us how many of those parts we have.

numerator   →   1   This fraction is called 'a third'. It means that something has been
denominator →   3   divided into 3 equal parts or thirds. We have 1 piece out of the 3.

odd numbers – whole numbers that cannot be divided exactly by two. Odd numbers always end in 1, 3, 5, 7 or 9.

place value – the 'value' of something is what it is worth. 'Place value' shows us the value of a digit depending on where in the number it appears:

	Th	H	T	U
4 is worth 4 units				4
40 is worth 4 tens			4	0
400 is worth 4 hundreds		4	0	0
4000 is worth 4 thousands	4	0	0	0

If there is a zero in a column it simply means that we haven't got any of these.

p.m. – when written after a time (for example, 9 p.m.), 'p.m.' stands for 'post meridian', which is another way of saying 'after midday'. So '9 p.m.' means 'nine o'clock in the evening'.

remainder – something left over. (9 divided by 2 = 4 with a remainder of 1)

right angle – an angle of 90 degrees (90°). Degrees are shown by the symbol °.

shape – the way something looks. Squares, triangles, circles, rectangles and ovals are all shapes.

From: **Mental Arithmetic Teacher's Guide** (ISBN 978 07217 1211 6). Copyright © Schofield & Sims Ltd, 2013. First published in the **I can do maths Teacher's Guide** by Andrew Dunn, copyright © Schofield & Sims Ltd, 2007. Published by Schofield & Sims Ltd, Dogley Mill, Fenay Bridge, Huddersfield HD8 0NQ, UK (www.schofieldandsims.co.uk).

The language of maths: Book 2

acute angle – an angle of less than 90 degrees (90°). Degrees are shown by the symbol °.

algebra – a 'grown-up' way of talking about number sentences that include letters in place of some numbers. If you were given a sum such as 6 + ? = 10, you would know that the missing number is 4 because 6 + 4 = 10. Algebra replaces the missing number with a letter (such as y), so the sentence would say 6 + y = 10. The answer would still be 4 because $y = 4$

circumference – the distance all the way round a circle.

diameter – a straight line drawn through the centre of a circle. It divides the circle in half.

direction – the directions N (north), S (south), E (east) and W (west) are known as the four points of the compass.

equation – a 'grown-up' word for a number sentence. In an equation, whatever comes before the = sign is worth the same as whatever comes after it. In other words, the two sides of the equation should equal one another. (5 = 3 + 2 *or* 2 × 6 = 12)

obtuse angle – an angle of more than 90 degrees (90°). Degrees are shown by the symbol °.

parallel lines – are the same distance apart from one another all the way along their length. They will never meet, no matter how long you make them.

radius – the radius of a circle is the length of a straight line drawn from the centre of the circle to its curved edge, as shown in the drawing below.

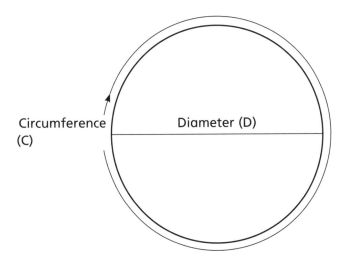

Circumference (C)

Diameter (D)

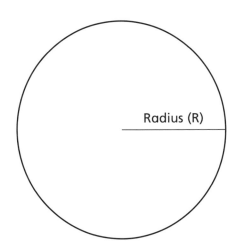

Radius (R)

Schofield & Sims Mental Arithmetic

The language of maths: Book 3

area – the amount of surface space inside the perimeter of a shape. We often measure area in square centimetres (cm^2) or square metres (m^2).

average – to find the average or mean of 3, 7 and 14, you have to find the total of the numbers (3 + 7 + 14 = 24). You then divide the total (24) by the number of items in your list (3). 24 divided by 3 = 8. The average is therefore 8. Use the same method to find averages of other lists of numbers.

capacity – the amount that something will hold. We may talk about the capacity of a glass or the capacity of a football stadium.

circle – a round two-dimensional (2-D) shape. A complete turn in a circle is 360 degrees (360°).

distance – the word we use to tell us how far it is from one place to another. One way of finding out a distance is to measure it using a ruler or measuring tape. To calculate a longer distance (for example, one that you would travel on a bike or in a car) you can use this formula: distance = time × speed.

perimeter – the distance all the way round the edge of something.

perpendicular – a line is perpendicular to another line if it meets it at right angles.

quadrilateral – a two-dimensional (2-D) shape with four straight sides and with internal (inside) angles that add up to 360 degrees (360°). Some quadrilaterals have special names (for example, 'square' or 'parallelogram').

rhombus – a two-dimensional (2-D) shape. It has four sides that are equal in length. Its opposite sides are parallel.

squared – a number that is squared is to be multiplied by itself (for example, '7 squared' is 7 × 7). We sometimes write squared with a very small number 2 placed after the number and raised up high. For example, '7 squared' is written as '7^2'.

triangle – a two-dimensional (2-D) shape with three straight sides and three angles that always add up to 180 degrees (180°). There are many different types of triangle (equilateral, isosceles, scalene, right-angled): try to find out about each type.

24-hour clock – the clock that we use for timetables. The 24-hour clock uses four digits. The first two are for hours and the second two are for minutes. For example, 1.30 p.m. is shown as 13:30 on the 24-hour clock.

From: **Mental Arithmetic Teacher's Guide** (ISBN 978 07217 1211 6). Copyright © Schofield & Sims Ltd, 2013. First published in the **I can do maths Teacher's Guide** by Andrew Dunn, copyright © Schofield & Sims Ltd, 2007. Published by Schofield & Sims Ltd, Dogley Mill, Fenay Bridge, Huddersfield HD8 0NQ, UK (www.schofieldandsims.co.uk).
This page may be photocopied after purchase for use within your school or institution only.

The language of maths: Book 4

arc – part of the circumference of a circle.

area of a triangle – to calculate the area of a triangle you use this formula:
area = half the base × the height. So if the base of the triangle was 6 cm and the height was 10 cm you would multiply 3 × 10 = 30 cm² (cm² means 'centimetres squared').

century – a period of 100 years. If you score 100 runs in cricket you score a century. A centurion was a Roman soldier in charge of 100 men.

factor – a whole number that divides exactly into another whole number. 2 is a factor of 6 because 2 divides into 6 with no remainder.

hexagon – a two-dimensional (2-D) shape with six sides.

octagon – a two-dimensional (2-D) shape with eight sides.

pentagon – a two-dimensional (2-D) shape with five sides.

per cent – 'out of a hundred'. If we have one hundred people and 10 of them have colds then 10 per cent have colds and 90 per cent do not. The symbol for per cent is '%'.

pi – the Greek letter 'p', which looks like this: π. We use it as a symbol to stand for a special number, 3.14, which we can use to find information about circles and angles. Ask your teacher to explain this to you.

ratio – if we have 4 blue marbles and 3 red marbles we can say that the ratio of blue marbles to red marbles is 4 to 3. Ratio is a way of comparing information.

reflex angles – are large angles that measure between 180° and 360°.

scale – sometimes in maths we draw things 'to scale'. We might draw a plan of a classroom by carefully measuring everything in it and then making them smaller on our plan. If a desk was 50 cm wide in real life we may draw it as 1 cm on our plan. We would say that we have a scale of 1 cm to 50 cm.

semicircle – half a circle.

symmetry – matching. If two halves of a shape or pattern match one another exactly then we can say that they 'have symmetry' or 'are symmetrical'.

volume – the amount of space that something occupies or takes up. We often measure it in cubic centimetres (cm³) or cubic metres (m³).

From: **Mental Arithmetic Teacher's Guide** (ISBN 978 07217 1211 6). Copyright © Schofield & Sims Ltd, 2013. First published in the **I can do maths Teacher's Guide** by Andrew Dunn, copyright © Schofield & Sims Ltd, 2007. Published by Schofield & Sims Ltd, Dogley Mill, Fenay Bridge, Huddersfield HD8 0NQ, UK (www.schofieldandsims.co.uk). **This page may be photocopied after purchase for use within your school or institution only.**

The language of maths: Book 5

approximation – a close estimate. If you are asked to give an approximate answer, you can give one that is close to the exact answer. For instance 18 is nearer to 20 than it is to 10, so 18 is approximately 20.

consecutive – things that follow one after another. For example, 6, 7, 8 and 9 are consecutive numbers. March, April and May are consecutive months.

hectare – 10 000 square metres.

inclusive – means 'including all those things mentioned'. So if you were asked, 'How many days from 1 March to 8 March inclusive?' you would include both 1 and 8 March in your calculations (making eight days). The opposite of inclusive is **exclusive**.

multiple – the multiple of a number can be divided exactly by that number. 4, 6, 8 and 10 are all multiples of 2 because 2 divides into them with no remainder.

negative number – a number less than zero. A negative number has a minus sign in front of it (–1, –2, etc.).

prime number – a number that divides by itself and 1 only. The first 10 prime numbers are 2, 3, 5, 7, 11, 13, 17, 19, 23 and 29.

prism – a prism is a three-dimensional (3-D) shape with two ends that are the same size and shape as one another.

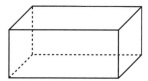 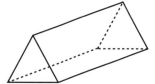 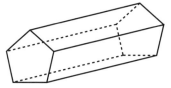

square number – the answer when a number has been multiplied by itself. For example, 4 is a square number; it has been made by multiplying 2 by itself. ($2 \times 2 = 4$ or $2^2 = 4$)

square root $\sqrt{}$ – the opposite of a square number. A square root is multiplied by itself to make a square. For example, the square root of 4 is 2 because $2 \times 2 = 4$; the square root of 9 is 3 because $3 \times 3 = 9$

Schofield & Sims Mental Arithmetic

The language of maths: Book 6

approximation – a close estimate. If you are asked to give an approximate answer, you can give one that is close to the exact answer. For instance 18 is nearer to 20 than it is to 10, so 18 is approximately 20.

consecutive – things that follow one after another. For example, 6, 7, 8 and 9 are consecutive numbers. March, April and May are consecutive months.

coordinates – letters or numbers that are sometimes used on graphs or maps to help us find the exact position of something.

decade – a period of 10 years.

decimal places – the number of digits after the decimal point. For example, you may be asked to write 6.92 to one decimal place (dp). You need to round the number so that there is only one place after the decimal point, and therefore 6.92 becomes 6.9

hectare – 10000 square metres.

imperial measures – before we used centimetres, metres, litres and kilograms (decimal measures) everyone in Britain used imperial units for measuring (for example: feet, yards, miles, pounds, stones, gallons).

inclusive – means 'including all those things mentioned'. So if you were asked, 'How many days from 1 March to 8 March inclusive?' you would include both 1 and 8 March in your calculations (making eight days). The opposite of inclusive is **exclusive**.

multiple – the multiple of a number can be divided exactly by that number. 4, 6, 8 and 10 are all multiples of 2 because 2 divides into them with no remainder.

negative number – a number less than zero. A negative number has a minus sign in front of it (–1, –2, etc.).

prime number – a number that divides by itself and 1 only. The first 10 prime numbers are 2, 3, 5, 7, 11, 13, 17, 19, 23 and 29.

prism – a prism is a three-dimensional (3-D) shape with two ends that are the same size and shape as one another.

significant figures – the number of digits needed to write a number that is accurate enough for a particular purpose. Your teacher will explain what this means.

square number – the answer when a number has been multiplied by itself. For example, 4 is a square number; it has been made by multiplying 2 by itself. ($2 \times 2 = 4$ *or* $2^2 = 4$)

square root √ – the opposite of a square number. A square root is multiplied by itself to make a square. For example, the square root of 4 is 2 because $2 \times 2 = 4$; the square root of 9 is 3 because $3 \times 3 = 9$

Units of measurement – and money

Length

Metric

10 millimetres (mm) = 1 centimetre (cm)

100 centimetres (cm) = 1 metre (m)

1000 metres (m) = 1 kilometre (km)

Imperial

12 inches = 1 foot

3 feet = 1 yard

Mass

Metric

1000 grams (g) = 1 kilogram (kg)

Imperial

16 ounces (oz) = 1 pound (lb)

14 pounds (lb) = 1 stone (st)

Capacity

Metric

1000 millilitres (ml) = 1 litre (l)

100 centilitres (cl) = 1 litre

Imperial

8 pints = 1 gallon

Money

Try to learn the shapes of these coins and how much each one is worth.

 1p 2p 5p 10p

 20p 50p £1

Remember that there are 100 pence (100p) in £1.

Number line: –10 to +10

Schofield & Sims Mental Arithmetic

Number line: 0 to 100

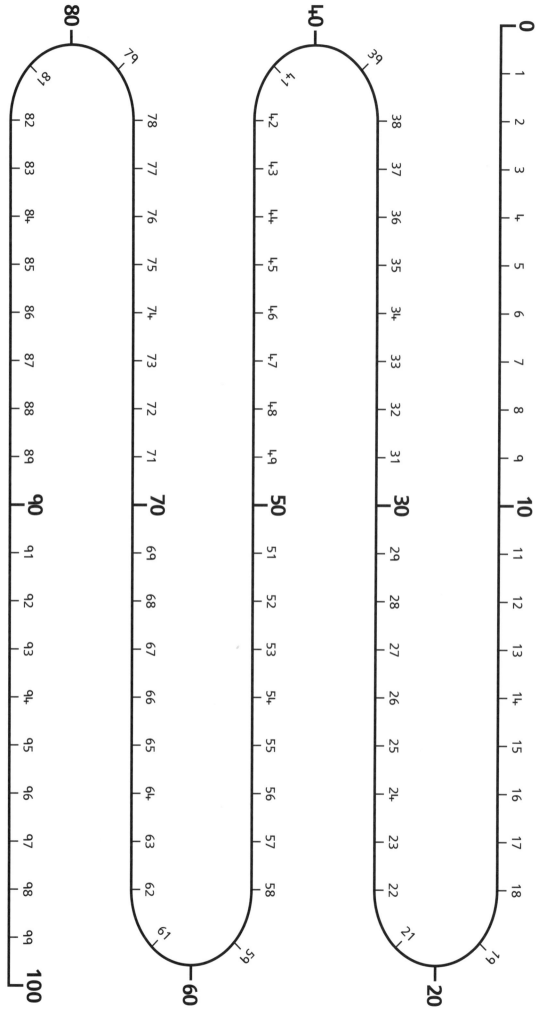

Counting square

1	2	3	4	5	6	7	8	9	10
11	12	13	14	15	16	17	18	19	20
21	22	23	24	25	26	27	28	29	30
31	32	33	34	35	36	37	38	39	40
41	42	43	44	45	46	47	48	49	50
51	52	53	54	55	56	57	58	59	60
61	62	63	64	65	66	67	68	69	70
71	72	73	74	75	76	77	78	79	80
81	82	83	84	85	86	87	88	89	90
91	92	93	94	95	96	97	98	99	100

From: **Mental Arithmetic Teacher's Guide** (ISBN 978 07217 1211 6). Copyright © Schofield & Sims Ltd, 2013. First published in the **I can do maths Teacher's Guide** by Andrew Dunn, copyright © Schofield & Sims Ltd, 2007. Published by Schofield & Sims Ltd, Dogley Mill, Fenay Bridge, Huddersfield HD8 0NQ, UK (www.schofieldandsims.co.uk).

Schofield & Sims Mental Arithmetic

Multiplication square

✕	1	2	3	4	5	6	7	8	9	10	11	12
1	1	2	3	4	5	6	7	8	9	10	11	12
2	2	4	6	8	10	12	14	16	18	20	22	24
3	3	6	9	12	15	18	21	24	27	30	33	36
4	4	8	12	16	20	24	28	32	36	40	44	48
5	5	10	15	20	25	30	35	40	45	50	55	60
6	6	12	18	24	30	36	42	48	54	60	66	72
7	7	14	21	28	35	42	49	56	63	70	77	84
8	8	16	24	32	40	48	56	64	72	80	88	96
9	9	18	27	36	45	54	63	72	81	90	99	108
10	10	20	30	40	50	60	70	80	90	100	110	120
11	11	22	33	44	55	66	77	88	99	110	121	132
12	12	24	36	48	60	72	84	96	108	120	132	144

From: **Mental Arithmetic Teacher's Guide** (ISBN 978 07217 1211 6). Copyright © Schofield & Sims Ltd, 2013. First published in the **I can do maths Teacher's Guide** by Andrew Dunn, copyright © Schofield & Sims Ltd, 2007. Published by Schofield & Sims Ltd, Dogley Mill, Fenay Bridge, Huddersfield HD8 0NQ, UK (www.schofieldandsims.co.uk). This page may be photocopied after purchase for use within your school or institution only.

Schofield & Sims Mental Arithmetic

Months of the year

Thirty days hath September

April, June, and November

All the rest have thirty-one

Excepting February alone

Which has but twenty-eight days clear

And twenty-nine in each leap year

January	31 days
February	28 days (29 in a leap year)
March	31 days
April	30 days
May	31 days
June	30 days
July	31 days
August	31 days
September	30 days
October	31 days
November	30 days
December	31 days

From: **Mental Arithmetic Teacher's Guide** (ISBN 978 07217 1211 6). Copyright © Schofield & Sims Ltd, 2013. First published in the **I can do maths Teacher's Guide** by Andrew Dunn, copyright © Schofield & Sims Ltd, 2007. Published by Schofield & Sims Ltd, Dogley Mill, Fenay Bridge, Huddersfield HD8 0NQ, UK (www.schofieldandsims.co.uk).
This page may be photocopied after purchase for use within your school or institution only.

Schofield & Sims Mental Arithmetic

Fractions chart

One whole

Two halves	Two halves

Three thirds	Three thirds	Three thirds

Four quarters	Four quarters	Four quarters	Four quarters

Five fifths	Five fifths	Five fifths	Five fifths	Five fifths

Six sixths	Six sixths	Six sixths	Six sixths	Six sixths	Six sixths

Seven sevenths	Seven sevenths	Seven sevenths	Seven sevenths	Seven sevenths	Seven sevenths	Seven sevenths

Eight eighths	Eight eighths	Eight eighths	Eight eighths	Eight eighths	Eight eighths	Eight eighths	Eight eighths

Nine ninths	Nine ninths	Nine ninths	Nine ninths	Nine ninths	Nine ninths	Nine ninths	Nine ninths	Nine ninths

Ten tenths	Ten tenths	Ten tenths	Ten tenths	Ten tenths	Ten tenths	Ten tenths	Ten tenths	Ten tenths	Ten tenths

From: **Mental Arithmetic Teacher's Guide** (ISBN 978 07217 1211 6). Copyright © Schofield & Sims Ltd, 2013. First published in the **I can do maths Teacher's Guide** by Andrew Dunn, copyright © Schofield & Sims Ltd, 2007. Published by Schofield & Sims Ltd, Dogley Mill, Fenay Bridge, Huddersfield HD8 0NQ, UK (www.schofieldandsims.co.uk).

Fraction equivalencies

	Percentage	Decimal
$\frac{1}{2}$	50%	0.5
$\frac{1}{3}$	33.3%	0.33…
$\frac{2}{3}$	66.6%	0.66…
$\frac{1}{4}$	25%	0.25
$\frac{3}{4}$	75%	0.75
$\frac{1}{5}$	20%	0.2
$\frac{2}{5}$	40%	0.4
$\frac{3}{5}$	60%	0.6
$\frac{4}{5}$	80%	0.8
$\frac{1}{10}$	10%	0.1
$\frac{3}{10}$	30%	0.3
$\frac{7}{10}$	70%	0.7
$\frac{9}{10}$	90%	0.9
$\frac{1}{20}$	5%	0.05
$\frac{1}{50}$	2%	0.02

From: **Mental Arithmetic Teacher's Guide** (ISBN 978 07217 1211 6). Copyright © Schofield & Sims Ltd, 2013. First published in the **I can do maths Teacher's Guide** by Andrew Dunn, copyright © Schofield & Sims Ltd, 2007. Published by Schofield & Sims Ltd, Dogley Mill, Fenay Bridge, Huddersfield HD8 0NQ, UK (www.schofieldandsims.co.uk).

Time

60 seconds	1 minute
15 minutes	$\frac{1}{4}$ of an hour
30 minutes	$\frac{1}{2}$ an hour
45 minutes	$\frac{3}{4}$ of an hour
60 minutes	1 hour
24 hours	1 day
7 days	1 week
52 weeks	1 year
365 days	1 year
10 years	1 decade
100 years	1 century

From: **Mental Arithmetic Teacher's Guide** (ISBN 978 07217 1211 6). Copyright © Schofield & Sims Ltd, 2013. First published in the **I can do maths Teacher's Guide** by Andrew Dunn, copyright © Schofield & Sims Ltd, 2007. Published by Schofield & Sims Ltd, Dogley Mill, Fenay Bridge, Huddersfield HD8 0NQ, UK (www.schofieldandsims.co.uk).

Ordering numbers

1	1st	first
2	2nd	second
3	3rd	third
4	4th	fourth
5	5th	fifth
6	6th	sixth
7	7th	seventh
8	8th	eighth
9	9th	ninth
10	10th	tenth

From: **Mental Arithmetic Teacher's Guide** (ISBN 978 07217 1211 6). Copyright © Schofield & Sims Ltd, 2013. First published in the **I can do maths Teacher's Guide** by Andrew Dunn, copyright © Schofield & Sims Ltd, 2007. Published by Schofield & Sims Ltd, Dogley Mill, Fenay Bridge, Huddersfield HD8 0NQ, UK (www.schofieldandsims.co.uk).
This page may be photocopied after purchase for use within your school or institution only.

Area

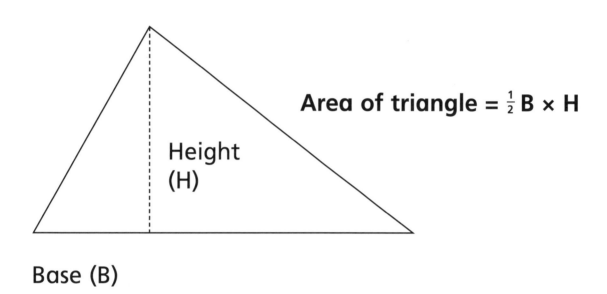

Area of rectangle = L × B

Breadth (B)

Length (L)

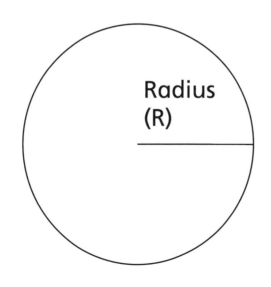

Area of triangle = $\frac{1}{2}$ B × H

Height (H)

Base (B)

Radius (R)

Area of circle = π × R²

(π or 'Pi' = 3.14)

*From: **Mental Arithmetic Teacher's Guide** (ISBN 978 07217 1211 6). Copyright © Schofield & Sims Ltd, 2013. First published in the **I can do maths Teacher's Guide** by Andrew Dunn, copyright © Schofield & Sims Ltd, 2007. Published by Schofield & Sims Ltd, Dogley Mill, Fenay Bridge, Huddersfield HD8 0NQ, UK (www.schofieldandsims.co.uk).*
This page may be photocopied after purchase for use within your school or institution only.

Perimeter

Perimeter of rectangle = 2 × L + 2 × B

Breadth (B)

Length (L)

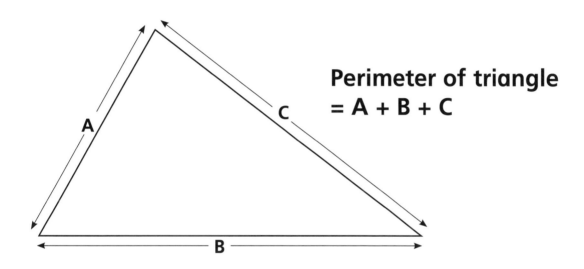

Perimeter of triangle = A + B + C

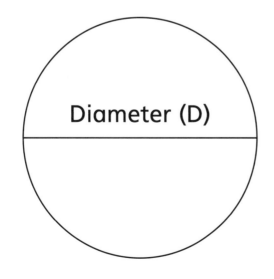

Diameter (D)

Perimeter of circle = π × D

(π or 'Pi' = 3.14)

Two-dimensional (2-D) shapes

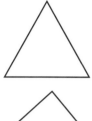 a **triangle** has
3 straight sides

 a **quadrilateral**
has 4 straight sides

 a **rectangle** is a
quadrilateral with
4 right angles

 a **square** has 4 right
angles and 4 sides
the same length

 a **pentagon** has
5 straight sides

 a **hexagon** has
6 straight sides

 an **octagon** has
8 straight sides

 a **circle** has 1 curved side

 a **semicircle** has 1 curved
and 1 straight side

Three-dimensional (3-D) shapes

 cone

 sphere

 cylinder

 cube

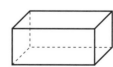 cuboid

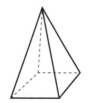 pyramid

Parts of a circle

From: **Mental Arithmetic Teacher's Guide** (ISBN 978 07217 1211 6). Copyright © Schofield & Sims Ltd, 2013. First published in the **I can do maths Teacher's Guide** by Andrew Dunn, copyright © Schofield & Sims Ltd, 2007. Published by Schofield & Sims Ltd, Dogley Mill, Fenay Bridge, Huddersfield HD8 0NQ, UK (www.schofieldandsims.co.uk).

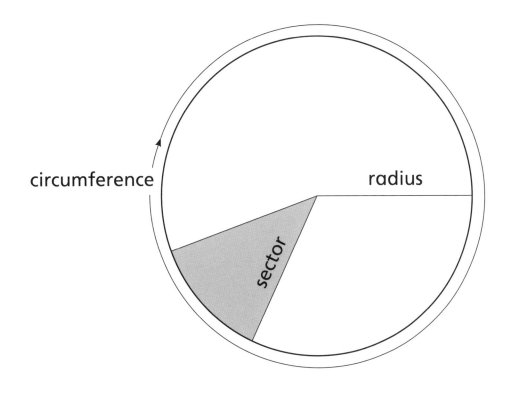

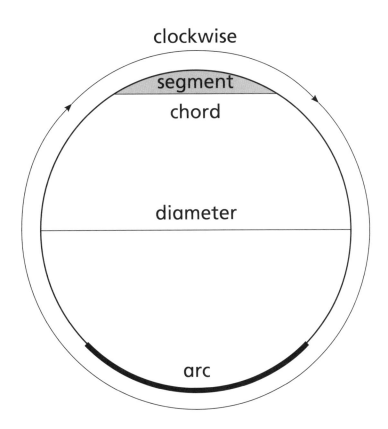

Coordinates

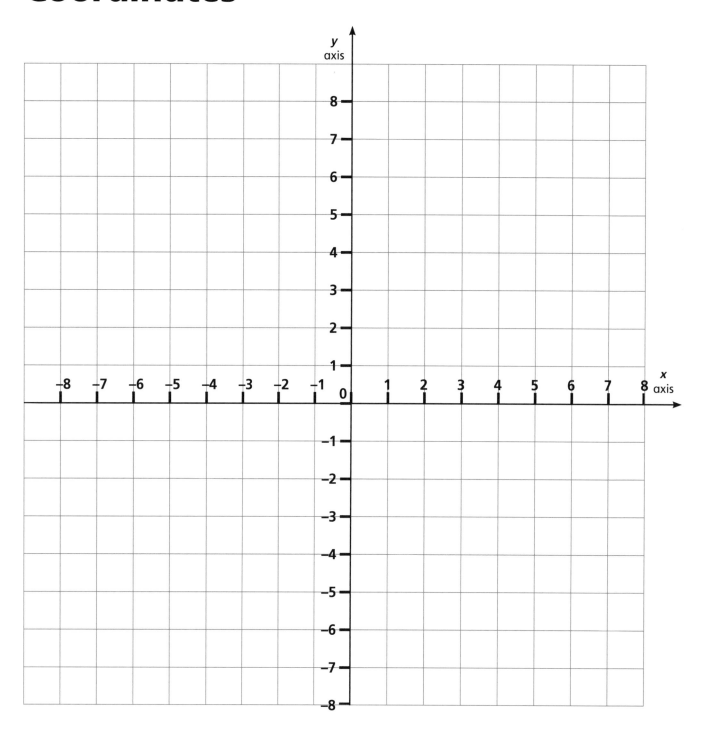

Glossary

a.m.
when written after a time (for example, '9 a.m.'), 'a.m.' stands for 'ante meridian', which is another way of saying 'before midday'. So '9 a.m.' means 'nine o'clock in the morning'.

acute angle
an angle of less than 90 degrees (90°). Degrees are shown by the symbol °.

addition
'counting up' or 'finding the sum of' two or more numbers. (3 add 3 = 6)

algebra
a way of talking about number sentences using letters in place of some numbers. If you were given a sum such as 6 + ? = 10, you would know that the missing number is 4 because 6 + 4 = 10. Algebra replaces the missing number with a letter (such as y), so the sentence would say 6 + y = 10. The answer would still be 4 because y = 4

altogether
to find how many there are altogether, add them all up. (10 + 2 + 3 = 15. There are 15 altogether.)

approximation
a close estimate. If you are asked to give an approximate answer, you can give one that is close to the exact answer. For instance, 18 is nearer to 20 than it is to 10, so 18 is approximately 20

arc
part of the circumference of a circle.

area
the amount of surface space inside the perimeter of a shape. We often measure area in square centimetres (cm²) or square metres (m²).

area of a triangle
to calculate the area of a triangle you use this formula: area = half the base × the height. So if the base of the triangle was 6 cm and the height was 10 cm you would multiply 3 × 10 = 30 cm² (cm² means 'centimetres squared').

average
to find the average or mean of 3, 7 and 14, you have to find the total of the numbers (3 + 7 + 14 = 24). You then divide the total (24) by the number of items in your list (3). 24 divided by 3 = 8. The average is therefore 8. Use the same method to find averages of other lists of numbers.

brackets
if a question has some numbers in brackets, you should work out what is in the brackets before you do the rest of the question. For example, in the calculation (7 × 4) + 3 you would multiply 7 × 4 before trying to add 3 to it. Your answer would be 31

capacity
the amount that something will hold. We may talk about the capacity of a glass or the capacity of a football stadium.

century
a period of 100 years. If you score 100 runs in cricket you score a century. A centurion was a Roman soldier in charge of 100 men.

circle
a round two-dimensional (2-D) shape. A complete turn in a circle is 360 degrees (360°).

circumference
the distance all the way round a circle.

consecutive
things that follow one after another. For example, 6, 7, 8 and 9 are consecutive numbers. March, April and May are consecutive months.

coordinates
letters or numbers that are sometimes used on graphs or maps to help us find the exact position of something.

decade
a period of 10 years.

decimal places	the number of digits after the decimal point. For example, you may be asked to write 6.92 to one decimal place (dp). You need to round the number so that there is only one place after the decimal point, and therefore 6.92 becomes 6.9
decrease	means 'make something less'. Decrease 3 by 2 and you get 1. You started with 3, you took 2 away, you have 1 left.
degree	the unit used to measure an angle. A degree is shown by the symbol °.
diameter	a straight line drawn through the centre of a circle. It divides the circle in half.
difference	to find the difference between numbers, compare them. There are two ways to find the difference between 8 and 3. Count on from the smaller number 3 to the larger number 8 or write down the larger amount and take the smaller amount away from it. The difference between 8 and 3 is 5
direction	the directions N (North), S (South), E (East) and W (West) are known as the four points of the compass.
distance	the word we use to tell us how far it is from one place to another. One way of finding out a distance is to measure it using a ruler or measuring tape. To calculate a longer distance (for example, one that you would travel on a bike or in a car) you can use this formula: distance = time × speed.
dividing	splitting things into equal groups. (Divide 6 by 2 = 3. You have split 6 into 2 equal groups, with 3 in each. 6 ÷ 2 = 3)
double	twice. When you double something you make it twice as big. Doubling is the same as multiplying by 2. So double 5 is 10 because 5 × 2 = 10
dozen	a dozen means 12, so 'I would like a dozen buns' means 'I would like 12 buns'.
equals	We use this sign instead of the words 'makes' or 'is the same as'. (You might say '5 add 3 = 8' or '5 add 3 is the same as 8' or '5 add 3 makes 8'.)
equation	another word for a number sentence. In an equation, whatever comes *before* the = sign is worth the same as whatever comes *after* it. In other words, the two sides of the equation should equal one another. (5 = 3 + 2 *or* 2 × 6 = 12)
estimate	a sensible guess.
even number	a whole number that can be divided exactly by 2. For example: 8 divided by 2 = 4, so 8 is an even number. 9 divided by 2 = 4 with 1 left over, so 9 is not an even number: it is an odd number. Even numbers always end in 0, 2, 4, 6 or 8
factor	a whole number that divides exactly into another whole number. 2 is a factor of 6 because 2 divides into 6 with no remainder.
fewer than	means 'less than'. (3 fewer than 7 is 4)
fraction	a part of something. The bottom number of a fraction is called the denominator. It tells us the fraction's name and how many equal parts something has been divided into. The top number of a fraction is called the numerator. It tells us how many of those parts we have.

Numerator → $\dfrac{1}{3}$ ← Denominator

This fraction is called 'a third'. It means that something has been divided into 3 equal parts or thirds. We have 1 piece out of the 3

Half ($\frac{1}{2}$) and a quarter ($\frac{1}{4}$) are also fractions. To find half ($\frac{1}{2}$) of something we divide it by 2. We halve it. (Half of 10 is 5) To find a quarter ($\frac{1}{4}$), divide something into four equal pieces, and each piece is called a quarter.

greater than	here is an example: 4 greater than 5 = 9
half	to find half of something we divide it by 2. We halve it. (Half of 10 is 5)
hectare	10 000 square metres.
hexagon	a two-dimensional (2-D) shape with six sides.
imperial measures	before we used centimetres, metres, litres and kilograms (decimal measures) everyone in Britain used imperial units for measuring (for example: feet, yards, miles, pounds, stones, gallons).
inclusive	including all those things mentioned. If you were asked, 'How many days from 1 March to 8 March inclusive?' you would include both 1 and 8 March in your calculations (making eight days). The opposite of inclusive is exclusive.
increase	if something is increased you have more of it. Increase 3 by 2 and you get 5
less	means 'fewer than' or 'not as many'. (4 less than 5 is 1)
minus	means 'take away'. (8 minus 5 = 3 or 8 − 5 = 3)
more than	here is an example: '6 more than 3' is the same as '6 and then 3 more'. (6 more than 3 = 9) How many more than 3 is 5? Answer: 2
multiple	the multiple of a number can be divided exactly by that number. 4, 6, 8 and 10 are all multiples of 2 because 2 divides into them with no remainder.
multiplication	a quick way to add up equal sets.
multiply	here is an example: multiply 2 by 6 = 12. So 2 × 6 means '2 multiplied by 6' or '2 times 6'.
negative number	a number less than zero. A negative number has a minus sign in front of it (−1, − 2, and so on).
obtuse angle	an angle of more than 90 degrees (90°). Degrees are shown by the symbol °.
octagon	a two-dimensional (2-D) shape with eight sides.
odd number	a whole number that cannot be divided exactly by two. Odd numbers always end in 1, 3, 5, 7 or 9
p.m.	when written after a time (for example, 9 p.m.), 'p.m.' stands for 'post meridian', which is another way of saying 'after midday'. So '9 p.m.' means 'nine o'clock in the evening'.
parallel lines	are the same distance apart from one another all the way along their length. They will never meet, no matter how long you make them.
pentagon	a two-dimensional (2-D) shape with five sides.
per cent	means 'out of a hundred'. If we have one hundred people and 10 of them have colds then 10 per cent have colds and 90 per cent do not. The symbol for per cent is %.
perimeter	the distance all the way round the edge of something.
perpendicular	a line is perpendicular to another line if it meets it at right angles.
pi	the Greek letter 'p', which looks like this: π. We use it as a symbol to stand for a special number, 3.14 …, which we can use to find information about circles and angles. Ask your teacher to explain this to you.

| place value | the 'value' of something is what it is worth. 'Place value' shows us the value of a digit depending on where in the number it appears: |

	Th	H	T	U
4 is worth 4 units				4
40 is worth 4 tens			4	0
400 is worth 4 hundred(s)		4	0	0
4000 is worth 4 thousand(s)	4	0	0	0

If there is a zero in a column it simply means that we haven't got any of these.

plus	means 'add'. (8 plus 8 = 16 *or* 8 + 8 = 16)
prime number	a number that divides by itself and 1 only. The first 10 prime numbers are 2, 3, 5, 7, 11, 13, 17, 19, 23 and 29
prism	a three-dimensional (3-D) shape with two ends that are the same size and shape as one another.
product	your answer when something has been multiplied. (3 × 4 = 12 so the product of 3 and 4 is 12)
quadrilateral	a two-dimensional (2-D) shape with four straight sides and with internal (inside) angles that add up to 360 degrees (360°). Some quadrilaterals have special names (for example, 'square' or 'parallelogram').
quarter	to find a quarter of something is to divide it into four equal pieces, and each piece is called a quarter.
radius	the radius of a circle is the length of a straight line drawn from the centre of the circle to its curved edge.
ratio	if we have 4 blue marbles and 3 red marbles we can say that the ratio of blue marbles to red marbles is 4 to 3. Ratio is a way of comparing information.
reflex angle	a large angle that measures between 180° and 360°.
remainder	something left over. (9 divided by 2 = 4 with a remainder of 1)
rhombus	a two-dimensional (2-D) shape. It has four sides that are equal in length. Its opposite sides are parallel.
right angle	an angle of 90 degrees (90°). Degrees are shown by the symbol °.
scale	sometimes in maths we draw things 'to scale'. We might draw a plan of a classroom by carefully measuring everything in it and then making them smaller on our plan. If a desk was 50 cm wide in real life we may draw it as 1 cm on our plan. We would say that we have a scale of 1 cm to 50 cm.
semicircle	half a circle.
shape	the way something looks. Squares, triangles, circles, rectangles and ovals are all shapes.
share	another way of 'dividing' or 'splitting up'. For example, share 10 between 5 people and they get 2 each. How many 2s in 8? Answer: 4
significant figures	the number of digits needed to write a number that is accurate enough for a particular purpose.

square number	the answer when a number has been multiplied by itself. For example, 4 is a square number. It has been made by multiplying 2 by itself. ($2 \times 2 = 4$ *or* $2^2 = 4$)
square root √	the opposite of a square number. A square root is multiplied by itself to make a square. For example, the square root of 4 is 2 because $2 \times 2 = 4$. The square root of 9 is 3 because $3 \times 3 = 9$
squared	a number that is squared is to be multiplied by itself (for example, '7 squared' is 7×7). We sometimes write squared with a very small number 2 placed after the number and raised up high. For example, '7 squared' is written as '7^2'.
subtraction	'taking away'. The answer is the number you have left. For example: We have 6 eggs. We subtract 2 so we take away 2. We have 4 left.
sum	to find the sum, add up all the numbers. (The sum of 2 and 4 = 6)
symmetry	if two halves of a shape or pattern match one another exactly then we can say that they 'have symmetry' or 'are symmetrical'.
take away	here is an example: 6 take away 4 = 2. Sometimes this is written as 'take 4 from 6'. Write down the 6 first so that you can take 4 away from it. ($6 - 4 = 2$) What is left when you take 2 from 4? Answer: 2
times	can mean 'multiplied by'. (4 times 2 is 8 *or* $4 \times 2 = 8$)
total	means 'count' or 'add'. (The total of 4, 2 and 3 = 9)
triangle	a two-dimensional (2-D) shape with three straight sides and three angles that always add up to 180 degrees (180°). There are many different types of triangle (equilateral, isosceles, scalene, right-angled).
volume	the amount of space that something occupies or takes up. We often measure it in cubic centimetres (cm^3) or cubic metres (m^3).
2-D	two-dimensional
3-D	three-dimensional
24-hour clock	the clock that we use for timetables. The 24-hour clock uses four digits. The first two are for hours and the second two are for minutes. For example, 1.30 p.m. is shown as 13:30 on the 24-hour clock.

Symbols

+ is the plus sign, for 'add'	= is the equals sign
− is the minus sign, for 'subtract' or 'take away'	√ is the square root sign
× is the multiplication sign, for 'multiply by' or 'times'	π is the pi sign
÷ is the division sign, for 'divide by'	° is the sign for degrees

Full list of the Schofield & Sims Mental Arithmetic books

Pupil books

For Key Stage 2:

Mental Arithmetic Introductory Book	978 07217 0798 3
Mental Arithmetic 1	978 07217 0799 0
Mental Arithmetic 2	978 07217 0800 3
Mental Arithmetic 3	978 07217 0801 0
Mental Arithmetic 4	978 07217 0802 7
Mental Arithmetic 5	978 07217 0803 4
Mental Arithmetic 6	978 07217 0804 1

The same pupil books, with covers designed for all other users:

Essential Mental Arithmetic 1	978 07217 1194 2
Essential Mental Arithmetic 2	978 07217 1195 9
Essential Mental Arithmetic 3	978 07217 1196 6
Essential Mental Arithmetic 4	978 07217 1197 3
Essential Mental Arithmetic 5	978 07217 1198 0
Essential Mental Arithmetic 6	978 07217 1199 7

Answers

Suitable for use with both **Mental Arithmetic** and **Essential Mental Arithmetic**:

Mental Arithmetic Introductory Book Answers	978 07217 0853 9
Mental Arithmetic 1 Answers	978 07217 0805 8
Mental Arithmetic 2 Answers	978 07217 0806 5
Mental Arithmetic 3 Answers	978 07217 0807 2
Mental Arithmetic 4 Answers	978 07217 0808 9
Mental Arithmetic 5 Answers	978 07217 0809 6
Mental Arithmetic 6 Answers	978 07217 0810 2

Teacher's Guide

This **Teacher's Guide** contains an **Entry test**, **Diagnostic checks** and many other useful items suitable for use with both **Mental Arithmetic** and **Essential Mental Arithmetic**:

Mental Arithmetic Teacher's Guide	978 07217 1211 6

Also available

First Mental Arithmetic is for pupils in Year 1 (Books 1 to 3) and Year 2 (Books 4 to 6). The Year 2 books are also suitable for some older pupils.

 For details of the **I can do** teaching method (which can be used with all the books mentioned on this page) and for information about **Mental Arithmetic's** companion series, **English Skills**, visit **www.schofieldandsims.co.uk**